Moving Medicine

Milton in his eighties

Moving Medicine

The Life and Work of Milton Trager, M.D.

Jack Liskin

Forword by Deane Juhan

1st Printing 1996
2nd Printing July, 2009, Published by United States Trager Association

Design by Susan Quasha
Typesetting by Laurie DiFalco

Photograph on page ii by Ann DiGioia.
Photograph on page 42 by Joan Phillips.
Photograph on page 66 by Didier Marie.
Photograph on page 154 by Carla Anette.
All other photographs are from Milton and Emily Trager's private collection.

Library of Congress Cataloging-in-Publication Data

Liskin, Jack.
    Moving Medicine: The Life and Work of Milton Trager, M.D. / Jack Liskin.
        p. cm.
    Includes bibliographical references and index.
    ISBN 0-88268-196-6 (cloth : alk. Paper)
    1. Trager, Milton. 2. Physicians–United States–Bibliography.
    3. Massage. I. Title.
    R154.T672L55 1996
    610'.92–dc20
        [B]   96-31343
                                                                  CIP

Printed in the U.S.A.

Contents

for
Sandy, Ahab, Aaron, and Jacob

Acknowledgements

Many individuals helped to bring this book to birth. Certainly, Milton Trager, whose life and work inspired it, and whose characteristically simple "Okay" gave me permission to proceed. Just as certainly, Emily Trager, whose tenacious caring triggered the idea of the book, and who consistently encouraged me and took me into her heart. Peter Lee, M.D., then Chairman of Family Medicine at the University of Southern California School of Medicine, supported my taking the sabbatical leave that provided the time and freedom to complete this labor; the love and good wishes of my students and staff in the Physician Assistant Program also nourished those sabbatical efforts. Turnley Walker graciously allowed me to use his partially completed chronicle of Milton's life, written in the early 1970s, as important foundational material for this book. Betty Fuller, founder of the Trager Institute, gave her heart fully to the effort, and Don Schwartz, the Institute's Executive Director, was generous and helpful every step of the way. Deane Juhan was consistently enthusiastic, encouraging, and collegial as the work proceeded, as was Michael Stulbarg. Many Trager practitioners, instructors, and students, in their passion for their work, gave my effort added meaning and importance. And some of Milton's remaining family: brother Dave and his daughter Barbara Traeger, Harold Rose, and sister-in-law Bobbi Kahan generously contributed their time and memories. Paul Benson, M.D., helped me with "authority." As always, my family and all my relations were the nurturing matrix out of which this creation emerged.

Foreword

Milton Trager developed his innovative approach to somatic therapy, movement re-education, and rehabilitation in the solitude of his private practice for nearly fifty years before teaching his unique skills to others. In his late eighties as this biography was being written, Dr. Trager has devoted his past fifteen years to the training of a growing number of students and Trager practitioners – now approximately two thousand – in the United States, Canada, and Europe. His absorption in both of these endeavors has been total, and for the most part far removed from the attention of the general public and the media.

As a result of this long and focussed development, his life, his work, and his teaching arrive in the public eye and the health care marketplace in a rich and full state of internal growth, with a broad spectrum of potential applications and an extensive track record of extraordinary effectiveness. This biography, then, articulates a remarkable life fully lived and an original work deeply explored and thoroughly fleshed out.

Although unique in its details and in its important therapeutic implications, Dr. Trager's story is in many ways emblematic of the emergence in his generation of a number of remarkable healers and their "alternative" approaches. Like Ida Rolf, his interest in and insights into the potentials of the human body for improvement and self-regulation came from many years of personal experience in a variety of movement disciplines. Like Moshe Feldenkrais and Matthias Alexander, the fundamental principles of his approach derived from his successful management of his own injuries and physical pathologies, conditions that could have been – should have been, from the medical perspective – permanently disabling. Like Deepak Chopra, his work springs from a deeply spiritual point of view furthered by a long immersion into Transcendental Meditation; and like Chopra, Dr. Trager has continually fused his spiritual practices with Western science and clinical practicality. And like so many such innovators, his ideas and his work long suffered the incomprehension and chilly incredulity of most of his scientific and medical peers.

This fusion of spiritual consciousness and the empirical methods of science, both rooted firmly in a down-to-earth, street-wise personality, is the principal theme and significance of Dr. Trager's life story. How a small scrappy street kid from Chicago stumbled into a hidden talent for healing, and how he developed that natural gift into an effective and significant modality of bodywork, movement rehabilitation, and emotional integration is truly an inspirational tale. It is a story that celebrates creativity and self-discipline in equal measure, and one that offers valuable insights for the active realization of our own talents as well as an appreciation of his.

This story is also a piece of the history of our growing understanding of the intimate and mutually causal relationships between the body and the mind. As such, Dr. Trager's work is not simply a new sort of treatment, but also one of the most arresting examples of a whole new kind of medicine. Innovative practitioners of his rare caliber have already begun to profoundly alter medical theory and practice for a wide range of traumatic, chronic, and degenerative conditions that have proved to be impervious to drugs, surgery, or technology. Dr. Trager is one of the discoverers whose work will help to transform mainstream health education and treatment in this country, help to turn last resort "alternatives" into "complements" of initial priority, and help to develop a system that is both vastly more humane and vastly less expensive.

It is a story that needs to be known, and one that is well told in the following pages by an author who has deeply explored both the man and the themes and principles underlying his work.

DEANE JUHAN
Mill Valley
March 1996

Prologue

I asked the sky to teach me
"Behold the beauty"
Thank you for the beauty.

I asked the rock to teach me
"Perservere in beauty"
Thank you for the beauty.

I asked the tree to teach me
"Rise up in beauty"
Thank you for the beauty.

I asked the mountain to teach me
"Stand in beauty"
Thank you for the beauty.

I asked the cloud to teach me
"Move in beauty"
Thank you for the beauty.

I asked Milton to teach me
"Feel the beauty"
Thank you for the beauty.

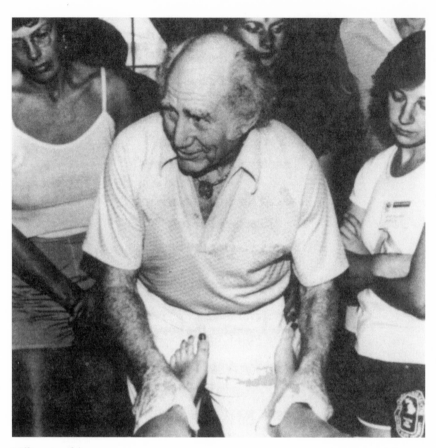

Milton teaching

Introduction

This is the story of an American original, a man so attuned to his internal rhythm and feeling – and to universal rhythm and feeling – that he developed, in isolation, over the course of several decades, a therapeutic method and art that is at once anachronistic, ahead of its time, and timeless. For America and other technologically advanced countries at the edge of the twenty-first century, his approach offers a link between discoveries in psychology and the neurosciences and the practical needs of clinicians and their patients.

For those who devote themselves to helping people who suffer with many of the common ailments of unknown cause or unsatisfying remedy, and to people with these illnesses, Milton Trager's approach offers insight and new possibilities for relief. But one must come to this particular understanding and healing in a personal, feeling way, a way far different from the typical manner of modern medicine, which has cut off part of its own feeling potential by its reliance on "scientific verisimilitude."

I came to know the man and his work out of my personal struggles, as many others had done before me, and I have written his story both as a symbol of success in that struggle and as a personal contribution to the advancement of knowledge in the art and science of medicine.

In January of 1988, my wife and I drove up for a weekend in Santa Barbara, California. We had been at odds for several months and were growing more and more estranged. I had, in the five years before that weekend, risen to the top of my profession as an educator of physician assistants, while Sandy had become a successful marriage and family therapist. We had three beautiful children and a lovely new home. Seven days a week, I arose at 5:30 AM and compulsively went to my local health club, alone, for strenuous aerobic exercises that I thought were essential for my well being. I was receiving classical voice training but was too anxious to enjoy performing, and I was feverishly writing intensely personal and mostly depressing poetry which I was desperate to publish. I was driven, miserable, full of anxiety, depressed, and as tense as a dog at the end of its leash. My neck and shoulders were stiff and ached constantly, and my lower back was frequently sore. I had also been recently diagnosed with glaucoma, an increase in the internal pressure of the eyes, which was increasing in severity despite the medications I was taking.

On the Sunday we were to head back to Los Angeles, after a strained and difficult two days, we browsed through the leisure living section of the local paper over morning coffee. That weekend the paper was featuring all of the various modalities of "bodywork" available in Santa Barbara: massage, manipulation, and magical rituals which I was interested in and skeptical of at the same time. I had received some hands-on work in relation to my voice training but was otherwise inexperienced in this realm of therapy. I scanned the brief descriptions until I read one I had never seen before that sounded unusual and appealing – Trager Approach®. Something about gentle rocking, rhythmic motion, easy, floating, cloudlike sensations.

On a sudden whim I suggested we treat ourselves to a session. I called the practitioner whose number was listed in the paper – Carla Montagno – and she was able to juggle her appointments and see us on short notice. We arrived at an old, rather shabby apartment court not knowing what to expect. At the door of her tiny apartment, a slight, somewhat somber woman greeted us. I waited and looked around the place while Sandy had her session in a cramped room off the living room. In an hour or so she emerged looking relaxed and contented. Carla then ushered me into the same room and instructed me to lie down on a low, padded table covered with a clean sheet.

She began with my neck, rocking it back and forth easily as my mind drifted away. She worked all around my body, ending at my lower back. As my pelvis moved hypnotically to and fro, I was suddenly suffused with the most intense warmth, which spread from the lower back to my entire pelvis and torso. A rush of sensual feeling filled me, followed by the most complete relief and relaxation I had ever experienced.

We paid and left, satisfied and happy. I promptly forgot the experience, or so I thought, until several months later when it suddenly occurred to me that I would love to do bodywork myself. I had always been physically oriented, and this hands-on approach to helping other people seemed extremely appealing. I began to explore several modalities until I remembered that serendipitous Trager session. I called Carla to ask about training. She gave me the number of an instructor in Los Angeles, Gary Brownlee, whom I immediately contacted. He had an introductory workshop coming up; I registered for it.

At the workshop, we explored very simple movements, getting in touch with the sensations they produced in our bodies. We also did some hands-on work with the other students, again exploring the feeling of moving different parts of their bodies with an easy, light, and soft touch. "This is the method for me," I thought at the time and signed up for the next available beginning training, in Palo Alto.

There, in a meeting hall near the campus of Stanford University, I discovered, over two long weekends, a new way of being – light, soft, easy, and free – which I had never known to be possible. No pushing, no hard work, no making things happen, but instead allowing them to happen. It was a revelation. And my neck and shoulders and back were completely at ease after a combination of tablework and directed movements. I had never in my life been able to tolerate walking slowly without feeling physically uncomfortable; I had prided myself on my speed and ability to outpace anyone. After one of the morning sessions, I spent forty minutes walking six short blocks, and it was the most enjoyable walk I had ever taken. I noticed and enjoyed everything—the sunlight, the sky, the trees and houses—but mostly I enjoyed the feeling of the most exquisite comfort in my body. Flying up for the second weekend of the training, I wrote a poem that spoke of the internal changes that this work had triggered.

For Life

fuzzy wing
blurred into birth
air dried wing
beyond cloud
before the spectral sun

the near is marked, clear
the distance bare
fly now

I was hooked. Still imprisoned in my pushed, compulsive, and urgent style, however, I inwardly determined that I must meet Milton Trager, of whom all the instructors and assistants spoke with such awe and respect. My hard-driving ways had made me successful and miserable in my professional life, and it was to be the ongoing lesson of Trager work to find a way to live differently. As a usually quick student, I was frustrated learning this approach because I could not pick it up faster than it allowed itself to be learned, and I was even more frustrated because only advanced students were allowed to have direct contact with Milton. All my pushing was proving useless.

Finally, in June of 1989, I was able to sign up for a Day With Milton, sponsored by the Trager Institute, the organization that coordinated all of the training and certification programs. Full of trepidation and anxiety, I drove down to Laguna Hills. Then, suddenly, there he was: easy, confident, serious, down to earth, and completely himself. With awe and nervousness, I intently watched every move he made, listened to every word he said, though I was too anxious to hear most of them. He sat astride a table, his back to me, working on a student's neck. I strained to absorb everything.

All at once, without warning, he looked over his shoulder directly at me and said with a shrug, "So I'm a phenomenon, so what?" Immediately the tension flowed out of me as I laughed at having been so accurately perceived and found out. But how had he known? Later he patted me on the head and said, "I'm so glad you're here."

My entire body grew warm at that statement, but why had he said it? Then he watched me walking and said, "There's a point that's driving you." He touched my mid-back, near the inner border of the left scapula. What had he seen? Only much later did I realize that he is constantly feeling and sensing everything around him, whether he is looking at it or not.

Wherever he worked, he exuded a quiet joy; it emerged not from pride in his own accomplishment but from the responsive changes in the people on the table, the letting go that they experienced. He made himself secondary. Everything he did seemed utterly simple; he attended fully to students' problem areas, with a serious yet casual curiosity. His hands were firm and confident, yet soft as petals. They held you fully, securely, allowing you to relax into them.

He had taken a special interest in me, calling me over repeatedly to let me feel something of note on people with whom he was working. I was embarrassed by the attention, but I was not about to reject it. He knew I worked at a medical school, and I knew that he wanted his work to be accepted in the medical field, but this attention to a stranger seemed extraordinary.

The first meeting proved fateful. After that first day, I seized every opportunity I could find to be with him, and his interest in me continued. I had much to learn about relaxation and ease and patience and how they could affect my health and well being, and still more to learn about helping others to find those feelings and weave them into their daily lives. Following countless struggles over my confidence and ability, I contrived to introduce the Trager Approach into my department's faculty practice at the University of Southern California School of Medicine, where I worked. I slowly developed a practice; family physicians, neurologists, rheumatologists, and physical therapists began to refer their patients to me.

In January of 1993, I was granted a sabbatical leave, part of which I intended to use to plan a clinical research project to help validate the Trager Approach in the medical literature. One day I travelled to Laguna to assist Milton and his wife Emily at a training. On the way back to their apartment, Emily mentioned that years ago a book had been started on Milton's life but had never been completed. She had followed Milton around for weeks at the time, asking him about his life, and had taken copious notes. A thought came to me. Perhaps I could take over the project.

Milton had never wanted a book about himself; his only interest was in doing and teaching his work. I asked him, "Don't you think it's about time that book was written? Would it be all right if I took a crack at it?" He uttered his one word answer – "Okay" – with an air of indifference and resignation.

Over the next several months, I gathered notes, half-completed manuscripts and letters; filmed and reviewed videotapes; and interviewed people who had known Milton or his work during the various stages of his life. He and Emily filled in gaps and corrected the inaccuracies in the course of numerous phone calls and visits. I felt a certain urgency in completing the project, as Milton was approaching his 85th year and was not in good health. There were many poignant moments, as the man whose story I wanted to tell, who sat on a sofa before me, was not well enough to tell his own story at any length. I felt helpless to help the man who had done so much for so many others, including me.

As I write this, medical practice and the Trager Approach each faces its particular crossroad. Will they travel together down one road, in partnership, or will each go its separate way, incomplete in itself? And will Milton see his wish fulfilled in his lifetime: to teach his work to doctors? He continues to teach, patiently and persistently, as he has done for the last sixty-five years, expecting but never demanding a response, asking only, "Well...how should it be?"

1

An Old Man Teaches

Twenty practitioners of an unusual art stand comfortably around a meeting room in a nondescript Best Western Motel off Interstate 5 in Southern California. Some of them chat quietly with a man in a wheelchair, a woman in crutches and leg braces, a child with spasmodic uncoordinated movements, and a man with wasted limbs. Every few minutes, in mid-conversation, their eyes dart quickly to the wide glass doorway leading to a sunny patio and parking area. The atmosphere is tinged with excited anticipation as they wait for the master teacher to arrive. They have travelled many miles to spend a few days absorbing the most subtle teachings of Milton Trager, what he calls Reflex Response work. Jim Day, from New Jersey, talks affectionately with a lovely seventeen-year-old girl with cerebral palsy whom he has been treating back home. A man in his mid-fifties with kind and gentle eyes, he exudes a compassionate warmth. Madeleine Terry and her colleague Bobby Nehman have come from Texas; their eyes are shining with vitality this morning. Others have journeyed to Laguna Hills from Washington, South Dakota, North Carolina, and Minnesota.

A woman with post-polio paralysis who has not walked without crutches for years waits anxiously for the workshop to begin. A man with severe muscular dystrophy is here, and another man with advanced Parkinson's disease. A young African-American woman with multiple sclerosis, an infant with cerebral palsy accompanied by her nervous parents, all have gathered here to be "models," to be touched by the man they have only heard about, the doctor who helps people move, who is known to work wonders with the lightest touch of his extraordinary hands.

These are veteran patients in the medical system. They have tried all the standard medical treatments, yet they continue to be disabled. They want relief; they want to walk, talk, run, play normally, or as normally as possible. They are willing to try something different, yet they don't want their hopes broken by some weird California therapy. All of them came because their practitioners—Trager practitioners—work with them in a way that is different from other approaches and hard to describe, yet so powerful and effective that they were willing to travel great distances, in some cases, to expose their bodies and be touched, moved, and handled by strangers in front of other onlooking strangers.

The practitioners have worked eight hours a day for four days already, learning the basics of this elusive and subtle reflex response work. They find it distinct from, yet somehow connected with, the approach they use daily in their practices, what they call the Trager Approach. These men and women have studied and practiced that method for years or they would not have been eligible to take this class. Now they gather daily in a fifteen by forty foot, low-ceilinged room, empty except for seven or eight massage tables and the chairs lining the walls. They have paid almost $1000 each to the Institute which organizes these trainings, in order to study with Milton and to work with severely impaired people, their own clients and others who volunteered to be teaching models.

It is April 1991, just past Milton's eighty-third birthday. He has developed and refined this work for sixty-five years, and he has trained several thousand students in the last sixteen. Later in the evening, the practitioners will honor him with a banquet and gifts. One of the students, Mary Jo Larsen, will perform a sensual belly dance for his enjoyment. Everyone will laugh as his wife Emily jumps up with mock anger to fend the dancer off with a fork when she moves her swaying hips too close to her dear husband. Milton will sit at the table and take the whole scene in peacefully, his neck ringed in fresh fragrant leis of plumeria flowers, specially ordered to remind him of his many happy years living in Hawaii.

This morning, however, no one is thinking beyond the next few minutes; every one waits for Milton's arrival, wondering what he will do and say. They understand that they cannot duplicate his genius; they wonder if they can achieve some fraction of the skill he has honed over decades of careful and patient work. Some of these practitioners have never seen the man but have learned his methods from instructors approved by the Trager Institute, the organization built around him by his devoted students.

A few miles south of the hotel where the students and models excitedly wait, expensive new tract homes dot the hilltops of Mission Viejo. On a south-facing bluff rests a large, muted pink apartment complex. The spacious, covered entrance is located on a side street off the broad boulevard that crosses the nearby Interstate. In the grand, high-ceilinged, modern lobby, Milton Trager quietly sits and waits. Old people walk slowly across the lobby, down long corridors tastefully decorated with potted plants and paintings with Jewish themes. The few people who notice him greet him respectfully: "Good morning, doctor." He nods silently in their direction.

To the right, two women manage a large reception station, answering phone calls from the residents and handling the many minor problems of life in a retirement home. One of them notices Dr. Trager sitting there; "Well, there's someone who never complains," she thinks. "Such a nice old man – hardly says a thing." Opposite the entrance, an easel supports a large map of the United States with tiny red flags pinned to it. Most of the flags cluster around the eastern seaboard and California. They represent the localities where the two hundred residents lived before coming to Heritage Pointe. Two little red flags stick into the nearby Pacific Ocean, where the Hawaiian Islands are crowded artificially close to the mainland so as to fit on the map. On one flag, Milton's name appears; on the other, Emily's.

Milton's walker stands by his chair. He and Emily have just finished breakfast in the large dining room down the far corridor. She is picking up the boxed lunch that the Filipino and Latino kitchen staff have packed for their outing. The residents stay active here; the staff is accustomed to packing lunches for their excursions to the local malls and doctors' offices. They're too busy now to ponder where Dr. Trager and Emily might be off to today; if they had the time, they would assume that the couple was about to head off shopping. They know him only as a nice old man who hardly ever talks, and her as a frail but colorful and astutely perceptive woman.

The Jewish men and women who live here in their small apartments, with terraces overlooking the lawn of an interior courtyard and a rarely used pool, have long since given up their careers in business or the professions. They have chosen to end their days in this comfortable environment, with its many planned activities, its attentive support staff, and its kosher food served in a communal dining room. A few of them have gone to a class that Milton was connected with, something with an odd name, but they didn't quite understand what it was all about or why a retired doctor would be interested in those strange movements they were asked to perform. Something about relaxation or feeling. All they feel are aches and pains, but they make the best of it and act friendly to everyone.

They wonder why Dr. Trager looks so serious all the time, why he talks so little, and why, as introspective as he seems, so many different young men and women come to visit him. And why do the visitors often wear shirts with that strange Oriental logo on it? They have heard rumors that he has helped other residents with medical problems, using some unusual technique. Of course, he is rather striking looking, they notice, with an unruly ring of white hair flung out around his head. And he looks so peaceful, almost noble in some curious way. They conclude that he must have been a popular doctor in his day, an interesting man, but so disabled now that he hardly ever goes anywhere. They notice that the girls packed a lunch for Emily and him today; they must be going shopping.

Emily guides her three-wheeled walker across the lobby toward Milton. Two plastic bags and a metal cane hang from it, one of the bags containing the freshly boxed food. She scans his face; she worries about him. A young woman comes through the double front doors and approaches them smiling. Their ride has arrived. Slowly Milton rises to his feet and pushes his own walker out the tall doors and over to her car. He and Emily laboriously seat themselves and fasten their seatbelts for the short drive to Laguna Hills. Once there, he abandons the walker. Gathering his energy, he shifts his weight from side to side in preparation and, with quiet concentration, begins the short walk across the familiar patio toward the curtained door.

Suddenly, a palpable hush falls on the roomful of students, assistants, and models. Without a word, it is understood that Milton is here. All eyes turn once more to the south door. The curtain billows in a light breeze. First Emily enters, looking regal in an azure and pink silk dress and scarf hinting of India, and, in another moment, treading lightly and soundlessly, Milton arrives. His white hair flares out, ringing an otherwise bald head. He is short, less than 5′6″, and his face is craggy, furrowed, and tough like an old boxer's face, but the skin is pink and soft. His intense blue eyes radiate seriousness, simplicity, and complete self-confidence. His arms, long and powerful despite his age, sway comfortably when he walks, as though he were feeling the air around him. His chest is stout, the whole torso muscular. Under a gray rayon jacket, he wears a tee shirt with a logo in Chinese script, slacks, and soft white shoes.

He accepts the greetings of one or two of his long time students with a soft smile and a twinkling glance, then moves to one of the chairs, which have been quickly arranged in a circle. There is in his quietness and seriousness a powerful sense of peacefulness, which infuses everyone in the room. They join him in the circle. Slowly, deliberately, one by one, he asks all of the practitioners to say a few words about their thoughts and feelings, and he listens with a still attentiveness that seems to emerge not only from his eyes and ears, but from his entire body.

Obviously overflowing with feeling, all of the practitioners blurt out something of their excitement, anxiety, or pleasure. To one, he comments briefly in response, something encouraging; to others, he simply nods his head or brings his hands together gently in acknowledgement. All eyes focus on him intently. He speaks to the practitioners about the nature of the work.

"Just be there with the person, intimately," he says. "Forget what I'm doing; just pick up my feeling. The point is what is registered in the person's mind, not what I'm doing. Once it has registered unconsciously, it is there forever. You're just there."

The group understands this language, these seemingly vague phrases; they have heard them many times. Now, with the opening circle completed, the work begins. Milton first asks all of the practitioners to bring themselves into a state of "hook-up," a connectedness with the life-giving force that surrounds them and is always available to them to and their clients. The practitioners who will be working this morning greet their models, bring them to the tables, and help them to lie down, and they begin the slow process of letting their hands become acquainted with the person's body: they explore and discover what moves easily and what doesn't move, and how the body moves; they feel how hard and tense the tissue is, or how soft. Their hands simultaneously sense the tissue and communicate with it, sending it repeated messages of spaciousness, length, softness, and freedom of motion.

Milton moves carefully from table to table, conserving his energy while observing the activity and feeling the manner in which the practitioners work, their attitude. He steps in to work with a baby with cerebral palsy. Gently he places her in the crawling position. She can only tremble there and sway slightly, as she is unable to crawl. Moving to the end of the table, near her feet, he softly touches and holds her right foot, pulling it so slightly that the traction is invisible to the observers' eyes. Nothing happens at first; he remains there, utterly calm. Suddenly, that foot and leg move forward three inches. He places his hand on the other foot; again a pause, this time a shorter one, and again the leg moves forward. Five, six, seven times he repeats the movement and then turns to the confused practitioner standing nearby and shrugs with a sly smile on his face, motioning for her to take over. The child's father, a chiropractor, stands huddled with his wife, their faces glowing, tears in their eyes. This is the first time their one-year-old baby has crawled on all fours.

The teacher casually moves on to the post-polio woman. She has been struggling awkwardly, inching her way forward, leaning heavily on crutches. Most of the time, she uses a wheelchair to get around. When Milton tells her to let the crutches go, she turns abruptly, panic in her eyes, and glances at her regular practitioner, who reassures her with a confident, knowing smile. She looks at Milton expectantly. Using one of the students to support her, and with infinite patience, Milton spends ten unhurried minutes helping her to find her point of balance. When he taps her left shoulder, she sways far to the right; when he taps her back, she lurches forward. Then, gradually, those touches dislodge her less and less, as her feet and legs begin to respond reflexively to those external messages, and she begins to re-establish her capacity to balance. He teaches her to soften her knees, to stop clutching the ground with her toes.

When at last she is standing unsupported, a huge beaming grin on her face, he tells her to move forward. By now most of the students have come close and stand watching raptly. There is a silent tension in the room. She begins haltingly. "One step, two steps, then balance; now once again," he encourages her. And she does it, stopping after each double step. The stops grow shorter as she builds self-assurance. Soon she has walked fifteen feet across the room and is trembling with excitement.

"That is four times more than I've walked on my own in nine years," she says, her voice quavering with emotion. Their eyes meet. Milton's eyes twinkle as he moves on, peaceful and pleased. The man with Parkinson's Disease learns for the first time how hard he has been struggling to do everything. His chest, stiff as plywood until now, begins to soften; he takes the first deep breath he has felt in years. And Milton keeps moving, with a touch here, a word there, or a nod of approval. The touch is silky, soft, warm, and assured, always unhurried and always right at the core of the problem. No one who feels that touch ever forgets it. He is feeling the body with his mind.

He lingers with one woman whose body responds well, releasing more tension with every touch. "I don't want to leave here," he exclaims, "because I'm really enjoying it! People ask why I do this work. It's because of tissue response. Such a dumb thing; the tissue responds, and I'm happy." Watching another student labor with too much intensity, he says softly, "Just give him the feeling of softness."

Wanting to use the dramatic balancing and walking episode they have just witnessed as a teaching tool, he calls the practitioners together to instruct them: people are always moving to achieve and maintain balance, he says. They cannot rest in balance, because balance, in movement and in the self, is dynamic. For those with poor balance, the practitioners must find what is unbalanced and stimulate their rebalancing response, of which they have lost awareness. To people with spasticity, they must show relaxation; to the flaccid ones, they must teach tone. To the rigid, they must demonstrate flexibility; to the hard, they must teach softness.

The practitioners concentrate on their work, inspired again by their teacher. All morning the air hums with the energy of bodies changing, softening, moving as they have not moved in years. Neither models nor practitioners fully understand how it all works, but they can feel it happening. One student will express the challenge of the process in his journal that night after working with a teenager with cerebral palsy.

> "What could I do with those spastic legs? So little. The
> trouble was accepting that little bit as enough. No one said
> I had to do more. Only I judged myself harshly. Yet, by
> the end of the session, she was much more relaxed than at
> the outset."

The Chinese feast that night in honor of Milton's birthday is more a celebration for the students than for him. As they shower him with loving wishes, he sits impassively, accepting it all, turned inward and content within himself. He had suffered a stroke only a few months before this class; his right side is neurologically damaged, but he says not a word about it. His words are only for teaching, always brief and to the point.

"It's the manner in which I touch..."

"I ask, 'Why is the arm so heavy?' I don't DO anything."

"Just be there with the tissue, intimately."

"What is soft?"

"I'm just there; I'm lucky."

Throughout the day, in the midst of the most intensive work, Milton frequently glances over to Emily, who sits in a lounge chair in the corner of the room, watching everything and talking to students when they approach her, teaching and encouraging them in her own way. He depends on her nearness for his well being. She expresses many personal things to students, which Milton rarely does. For him, the work is all-important. "How are you, Emily?", he asks, looking up for a moment from the neck he is rocking rhythmically back and forth.

At the closing circle, after the day's work is done and the models have left with their families and friends, Cathy Hammond, a long time practitioner and instructor, haltingly expresses her gnawing concern about a time when he can no longer teach.

"I still have a lot to give," Milton Trager responds.

Helping a child with cerebral palsy, 1937

2

The Boxer Has A Gift

One deep breath. A single breath in 1924 inspired and impelled the work that would last a lifetime. Milton's family had just severed its connections with cold, hard Chicago and had moved to Miami, Florida in search of a better life. At age sixteen, Milton had long since dropped out of school. His parents needed the children's help and, as usual, he dutifully did his part to support the family's new beginning. In the booming Miami of the '20s, few men sought postal jobs at sixty-five cents an hour; Milton lied about his age and was quickly hired as a mail carrier, working East Flagler Street. He accepted his workaday role with no particular ambition and performed his duties quietly.

Every day at his post office, he passed a bulletin board covered with notices for employees. Some of them offered tips on caring for the feet, the eyes, or other parts of the body. One day young Milton, passing the board as usual, noticed a sign which read, "Take a deep breath." Following standard procedure, he initialled the message and left. The next day he noticed the sign again. Finding himself alone, he lowered his mailbag, paused, and breathed. Many years later, he would say: "That was the beginning of me."

"I'm not sure I understand even now why and how it happened that way, so quickly. I guess I was ready. After so long, I was ready. The right moment. For the first time I felt me. I was almost afraid to take another breath, afraid somebody would be there, laughing. But it was like I was invisible, and I plunged on. The sensation became fuller, stimulation at its best. I got higher and higher. And the important thing is, it stuck. The way a true discovery always does, I suppose. It was the first edge of all I was going to discover about my body and, through my body, about me."

The other mail carriers had only stopped to sign the notice and go about their business; Milton had paused, in the midst of the deadening daily routine, to explore and feel profoundly the most basic of human voluntary actions – breathing – and, in that moment, he discovered an internal galaxy that he would continue to explore the rest of his days. Slowly, over the course of thirteen years in Miami, Milton built a foundation on this new ground of understanding. He had no ambitions, only sensations that propelled him from one discovery to the next.

Always smaller than other children his age, even at birth, he had never developed physically in his home town of Chicago, but he was fascinated with all things physical even then. His family lived on Chicago's north side, in a rough but not poor section of town near the Sheraton Hotel, surrounded by Irish neighbors. The Irish kids were tough and not friendly to the Jewish Traegers; Milton, his three brothers, and sister were forced to fight for their safety in response to verbal taunts and physical attacks. They often travelled by alleyway rather than risk the exposure of the streets. Milton liked using his natural agility, fleetness of foot, and quiet toughness to earn a measure of safety and respect. Their Catholic neighbors at least respected their observance of the Jewish holidays. The local priest even visited occasionally; the senior Traeger, however, had no great fondness for him.

A devout Jew born in Warsaw, Milton's father was a master tailor with a reputation for his fine craftsmanship. A hard working and infinitely patient man, Hyman Traeger could tailor a jacket to fit a hunchback's hump perfectly, without a wrinkle, and he was paid handsomely when such a coat was needed. The family was orthodox and kept a kosher house; the elder Traeger helped to found Chicago's first northside synagogue. His wife, Bertha, was Lithuanian; the couple had come to the United States only a few years before she gave birth to Milton in 1908, settling first in New York's Lower East Side before moving to Illinois. In this adopted country, their world was confined mostly to work and family. With five small children to support, the immigrant parents labored all week, he in his shop and she at home. She cooked, went to the synagogue regularly, and showered love on the children.

Milton spent many childhood days in his father's workshop. Helpful even at that young age, he enjoyed spotting and picking up with his deft fingers the tailor's pins, which were perennially scattered on the floor. Delivering them dutifully to his father, he always received in return a gentle pat on the head and a loving, "Lucky boy." Somehow that appellation became a family nickname for the youngster, spoken with tenderness. He could not understand it at the time; he felt neither particularly lucky nor particularly talented.

He revered his father and greatly admired his older brothers, especially Sam, who shared his physical interests and spent time with him. Though athletically inclined, Milton was rather frail and susceptible to allergies. Perhaps for that reason he was sometimes left behind when his brothers and father went out together, in Chicago and later in Miami, leaving him feeling somehow unacceptable and different. Or perhaps it was his own dreamy, internal absorption that set him apart, the same faraway dreaminess that made it hard for him to take an interest in school and the structured concentration it required.

At thirteen, he celebrated the Bar Mitzvah ritual according to tradition, but he had no more interest in religious scholarship than in secular learning. His mind was on the moving body. His grammar school had a swimming pool, and he delighted in the freedom of movement that the water made possible. The brothers also sneaked into the Sheraton's pool when they could. The small, reddish-blond boy was fast; he loved to run and tumble acrobatically. He and Sam scavenged an old mattress from an alley and practiced stunts in the backyard. Sam competed on the high school gymnastics team and introduced him to the coach, encouraging him to join.

While he could quickly match the flips and leaps Sam taught him, Milton didn't want to compete and never made the team. In fact, after a year of dismal grades, he dropped out of high school altogether and, armed with nothing more than an eighth grade education, set out to make his way in the world. Friendly but not outgoing, he kept to the neighborhood, close to his relations who were also his only real friends. He considered himself to be fully American, but he kept close to the family fold in the Old World way. After work and on weekends, they sang together, brother Joe providing the sheet music, brother Dave playing guitar and piano, and sister Sarah strumming the mandolin.

He had always pitched in willingly at the household chores, hauling ashes and doing the heaviest work. While in school he had also contributed a few dollars to the family coffers by running errands, selling papers, and doing cleanup work. Now he had to join the regular labor force; he found hard, dead-end jobs in stifling factories or wherever work was available in the neighborhood, never moving linearly from one to the next, certainly not with any plan, but instead drifting, taking what came his way.

On weekends, however, a window opened to possibilities of a less dreary world when fourteen-year-old Milton wandered into the Bryn Mawr Theater, a small, shabby auditorium down the street from his house. Owned by the gangster, Yellow Kid Weil, it featured vaudeville acts on the weekend, movies during the week. Milton was powerfully attracted. He began to quietly hang around the theater. The stagehands, who, without counterweights, were constantly struggling with the heavy curtain and scenery, noticed the small, wiry teenager one day. Soon he was climbing the lofts for the crew, scrambling along the ropes and wires, acting as human counterweight for the curtains and scenery they raised and lowered during the shows. He was apparently fearless and never tired of helping them.

He became a regular, running errands, doing odd jobs, earning a little side money for the family. He basked in the free and exciting world of the stage. The colorful, long-legged dancers treated him sweetly as a kind of mascot. They lounged about comfortably half-naked in his presence and let him fasten their bras on occasion. Milton watched wide-eyed; he had never seen anything like it. It was heady and exciting work for a quiet Chicago kid from an immigrant family. Thrilled by the acrobatic acts, Milton resolved inwardly to become an acrobat too. Every week, after the shows, he and Sam practiced the stunts that had captivated him at the theater.

Milton didn't know at the time how quickly his resolution would be realized. His father suffered from hay fever; Milton had the same allergic susceptibility, and the Chicago climate aggravated it. Life in Chicago was generally hard and not getting much better. Stories of the mild Florida climate wafted north along with tales of riches to be made there. His family never expected riches; they expected to work hard but thought they might thrive better in a more temperate region. The senior Traeger and oldest son Joe decided to pave the way south, with the rest of the family to follow soon after. Milton had never journeyed beyond Chicago and knew nothing about Florida; when the family moved, the dutiful son simply went along.

Even the mild, fresh air of Miami didn't suit Milton at first. The postal work was tiring; he looked pale and weak. The family lived in cramped quarters without air conditioning above Hyman's shop, sleeping in shifts. Shortly after his moment of self-discovery at the post office bulletin board, however, he secured a transfer to a Miami Beach mail route and began spending his spare hours on the sand. He left the house at 7:30 each day and finished his route by 3:30 in the afternoon. Then it was off to the beach. There he was joined some days by his brother Sam, after his own workday of pressing and delivering clothes for their father, and they spent the afternoons until sunset tumbling, running, and playing. Milton had never experienced so much pure pleasure. The ever-changing sensations in his body absorbed him entirely. He kept exploring, reaching with curiosity for his physical limits, then transcending them by some new discovery, some new way of manipulating his own developing body. Time meant nothing to him, so passionately absorbed was he with the possibilities, with the unknown potential inside him.

He felt his muscles growing, and their potential development intrigued him also. Milton became "muscle-happy." From 1925 to 1937, while he continued to ply his mail route, he gradually honed his body into both a living sculpture and a high performance machine, a unique and highly specialized one. At first, he took pleasure in simply growing and shaping his muscles; he liked showing them off, too. Physical culture was in one of its early heydays; like many other young men, he followed the precepts of strongman and publisher Bernarr McFadden, who preached the gospel of a strong and healthy body.

Soon, however, Milton put aside his infatuation with muscles for their own sake. On the beach one day, he chanced to meet his idol McFadden; the famous man approached him to praise his body and his fancy footwork. Milton expressed some disappointment that the older man's body was not as muscly as he had expected. McFadden, smiling, put his arm around the youngster's shoulders and told him, "I guess as I grew older some of my muscles turned into brains." That got Milton thinking.

He slowly began to recognize the tension that he had been carrying in his over-inflated muscles. Gradually, over months and years, his movements began to reflect a changing consciousness. He asked himself, "How can this motion be made more beautiful, more harmonious?" As he moved nimbly over the hard sand left behind by the ebb tide, hearing the water splashing the shore, he sometimes felt himself drawn into the hypnotic rhythms of the ocean. He began to move to those rhythms, swinging his arms, swaying, feeling the sensations of an ever more subtle peacefulness entering him, feeling himself at one with the waves.

Even the acrobatics changed. Every Sunday, he and Sam performed at the beach. By this time, they were well known locally, and a crowd of would-be acrobats watched and followed them. One Sunday, Sam said, "Let's see who can jump the highest." Without thinking, Milton replied, "Let's see who can land the softest. What can be softer?" The spontaneous question surprised him and further spurred his shift of thinking, opening doors to new movements marked by their effortlessness, by the surrendering of tension.

Milton began to invent movements that evoked the qualities of softness, ease, and lightness even more, and to teach them. At the beach, he always attracted aspiring young acrobats who admired his abilities and wanted to learn from him. A natural teacher, he began to demonstrate his approach and teach these new movements as warm-up exercises for his acrobatic disciples, especially the younger ones of whom he was particularly fond. As they circled him, he moved in this new, more graceful way, projecting his internal sense of rhythmic motion and body awareness, letting the others pick it up from him. He was consciously tuning his body to ever finer and more subtle inner feelings, allowing the movements themselves to carry him along. His audience of students grew as he developed in this gradual, unhurried, exploratory way.

"They were receiving it in the most natural and direct way. It's still the key. It's the base I've worked from in nearly all I've developed.

"My beach period went on for years, several important years, no need inside me to hurry, to get somewhere. I was always a slow developer, with girls and with all relationships and goals. Some sort of pure physical activity would grab me and I would go along with it, allow it to take me along into some level of understanding and meaning. No hurry. I suppose it was the only way I could develop something deep. It had to be all together and move forward, somewhere, at its own pace. There was no need to hustle myself anywhere for anything. I had the feeling, I suppose, that it would all come to me, what I really wanted, or that I'd meet it somewhere, when I was ready."

Milton's explorations took an unexpected turn when a co-worker suggested that, with his agility and strength, he should look into the local boxing scene. It wasn't until months later that he followed that suggestion. He finally walked into the gym sometime before his 18th birthday, figuring that he might learn enough to make a few dollars and help his family. The new sensations and movements enthralled Milton immediately. Somehow it reminded him of the action at the old Bryn Mawr Theater he had loved so well in Chicago. He liked the naturalness and simplicity of the boxers and their art; soon he was a regular at the YMCA where they trained. He had never seen a prizefight and almost forgot about the fighting, absorbed as he was by the footwork and the strange dance of the boxing ring. He imitated the fighters' movements and skipped rope, enjoying the feeling of it all. Soon, however, his agility, strength, and quickness caught the eye of Mickey Martin, an ex-fighter from Wheeling, West Virginia who managed and promoted some of the local talent.

"Hey kid, you move pretty good. You wanna fight?"

"Whaddaya think I'm doing?" Milton answered roughly, adopting the speaking style of his new companions.

"Would you like me to take you on, get you some fights?"

"Sure."

Milton began training under Mickey's hand, still mainly for the pleasure of using his body in this novel way. He had never considered the full implications of his actions and was surprised when Mickey informed him that he had arranged his first fight. When Milton showed he could handle himself in the ring, Mickey set up more fights. He moved exceptionally well; although he never won definitively, he wasn't losing either, and he showed plenty of heart. At home, Milton downplayed the danger of his new sport, knowing full well that his parents would never approve of it otherwise. After ten fights, he met his match in the form of "Battling Dundee" and arrived home battered, cut, and bruised; his mother went wild and put a quick end to the young pugilist's budding career. It was clear to Mickey anyway that Milton did not have the killer instinct of a real fighter. It was the fighter's moves – the dance – that attracted and pleased him. He had no desire to beat up an opponent.

A seemingly small incident during those boxing days proved fateful. It hinted for the first time at the direction in which Milton's natural talents would propel him. Mickey routinely rubbed his fighters down after a vigorous workout to relax the muscles. One day, noticing that his manager looked tired, Milton turned the tables and had him lie down for a massage. Having never touched another body in this way, he simply let his hands do whatever felt right, almost unconsciously. Suddenly Mickey bolted upright and turned to look at him.

"How did you learn to do that?!"

"You taught me, Mick."

"I never taught you anything like that!"

"How the hell do you think I learned it then?" Milton fired back, confused.

"I don't know, kid, but I'm telling you, you got hands."

"I do?"

Intrigued and pleased by this unexpected and enthusiastic response to something he had never ventured to do before, Milton went home and approached his father, who had been suffering from sciatic pain for two years without relief. He wanted to see if he could help him too. "Lay down, Pa," he said, using the two word phrase he would repeat thousands of times in the years to come. There, on the dining room table, again without a clue about what to do or how, he began moving his father's back and legs. Yes, he felt better. After four such treatments, the pain vanished, never to return. This was exciting and fascinating; Milton grew curious. What else might he accomplish using his hands this way? Whom else might he help?

"My father would have to be called my first patient. A wonderful accident, because he was my father. He helped me in deep ways, as I was helping him. I revered my father, his spirit, his love for others, his hard, unending work for his family. And his body. It has always been that way for me; the body must be included, with all that is strange and real and marvelous about it. My father helped me to feel a reverence for the body of each patient who would come to me. This, too, would become basic in all I would learn and be able to do."

In those years, many vacationers in Miami who had sick or crippled children brought them along for the therapeutic benefits of sunshine and fresh air. It was a time of polio epidemics; paralyzed children were a common sight. Milton's curiosity overwhelmed his normal shyness, and he began to approach disabled children and their attendants to ask if he could "play" with them. Day after day he experimented with those who permitted it, at first simply holding and feeling the lifeless or spastic muscles, feeling what they seemed to lack, then gradually, intuitively manipulating the tissues, continuing to feel his way in until, out of somewhere, came the flicker of a response. With extraordinary patience, he reinforced that response, evoking more and more movement. By the time he was nineteen, Milton had gotten his first polio-stricken child to walk, a child who had been paralyzed for four years. Milton was hooked.

He became a keen observer of gait and movement. After a while, he could assess a person's problem and its source at a glance. He worked now on anyone with a visible problem who would allow it, forgetting his shyness in the passion of his desire to help and to learn more. There were many more children with post-polio paralysis to work on, and he was soon consistently able to increase their capacity for movement. There were also kids with cerebral palsy whose spastic limbs he was able to relax and straighten. From the fight world came the daughter of Tex Rickard, Jack Dempsey's fight promoter. From the beach crowd came other referrals. He was beginning to earn a reputation.

With his increasing understanding of human movement and blocks to movement, he was able at times to help people without touching them. He noticed one young girl who had lost the use of her left arm; curious about her condition, he asked permission to play with her. At first befriending and casually playing with her, he then tossed a ball her way. She immediately rolled it back, using her right arm. He pushed it back, over and over, until she was hypnotically absorbed in the game. Then, at the correctly intuited instant, he rolled the ball to her left hand. Without thinking, she raised that arm and pushed the ball back. Hiding his joy for the moment, he repeated the act, until both her arms were alternating freely, for the first time, in this new game.

There were frustrations as well. Milton found that his successes were not universally appreciated. Not everyone had the patience required for his painstaking work. He resented it when parents of children he had gotten to stand and haltingly walk for the first time immediately sat their children back down in their wheelchairs. "Well, the doctors say he'll never walk, so why build up false hopes," they said, denying the evidence before their eyes, scorning and depreciating Milton's efforts.

Still, the successes outweighed the disappointments, and, though always modest, Milton enjoyed his spreading local fame. He did not promote himself as other men might have done in an effort to cash in on their skills, proclaiming themselves healers and thwarting the development of their natural gifts in the process. Milton's habitual reticence, modesty, and unhurried style served him well here; it allowed him to nurture and develop his inexplicable new talent over the next ten years. He accepted no money for his work; it was a sidelight, a curious and intensely interesting one, but to him it was nothing special, and he was nothing special. He tended to run from the admiration and rewards offered by the grateful parents of children he helped; rather he continued to watch, to explore, to discover, and to feel his way along. People in the neighborhood knew he had an unusual skill, but they accepted it as he did, as another oddity of their resort town life.

Milton's fascination with rhythm and movement, balance and grace, now led him down new paths. His beach acrobatics, coupled with the boxer's fancy footwork and his deep sense of rhythm, naturally flowed into dance. As with everything else connected to movement, he threw himself fully into this new avocation, experimenting, creating steps and moves, exploring his limits and the rhythms of his own character through his dancing. Soon he was frequenting Miami's dance halls; not much later he was coaxed into performing professionally in hotel and theater shows. He specialized in the acrobatic leaps and splits that he had perfected at the beach. His frenetic and spirited act thrilled crowds at hotels like the Deauville and at the racetrack, where he was paid to perform. There were times, however, when deeper, more complex, and disturbing facets of Milton's personality emerged, evoked by the dark rhythms in melodies like "Mood Indigo." As always, he freely gave time to the usual admirers, teaching them the dance moves and steps that he was developing.

All the while he continued to deliver mail during the day, now on a bicycle in the more affluent parts of town. In the mansions of Palm Island, he lightly touched some of the famous and powerful people of the day: Sophie Tucker, Al Capone, and J.C. Penney were among his clients. Milton's joy of movement, and his developing confidence, spilled over into his regular job. He used his bicycle acrobatically, balancing on the handlebars in a handstand as he approached a mailbox or gracefully flipping off the bike. He added song to his routine, crooning out greetings and goodbyes as he passed. His curious antics made him a local celebrity in yet another neighborhood and a cherished character along the mail route.

At the same time, on the other coast, Hollywood, like Miami, was also booming; movie newsreels were opening the eyes of Americans to the varieties of experience to be found in their country. Always on the lookout for entertaining material, three of the large studios found Milton and filmed sequences of "The Singing Mailman," as he came to be known. It was the first time his fame had spread beyond the beach, as millions watched his bicycle antics, mailbag slung over his shoulders, against a backdrop of white sand and bathing beauties.

Friends and family were nudging Milton in the direction of a career in entertainment, beyond his local celebrity. Milton, too, felt somehow that this phase of his development had peaked. During his Miami years, he had changed from a frail, shy, inwardly focussed child to a strong, multi-talented, and confident – even flamboyant – man. He was posing as a photographer's model and had bought an old, open cockpit race car from the track where he danced professionally. He had also had his first romantic involvement by that time. Perhaps, he thought, the moment had arrived to look beyond the edges of his beach town. Maybe he could make it in Hollywood. Yet it was not strong ambition that drove him; rather, he was compelled only to explore his passionate interests further, to explore himself further. In 1937, he said goodbye to his beloved family and drove west toward a new phase of his life, which included a newly shortened name: Trager. His brother Sam, remembering those Miami days, said of Milton:

"I can tell you the way it was for Milt, from the beginning all the way through. He had no affectations. He is the only human being I have ever known who is truly that way. Always was. Not just that he could not be a phony, although he couldn't. It was deeper than that. Completely natural, completely himself. If he liked something, he did it with all he had. If he didn't, he just walked quietly away. He could do many things, with his body—wonderful, wild, and crazy – but it was never showing off because it was completely him. He couldn't be a showoff, wasn't in him. Absolutely no affectations. None. I think that's what made some people believe he was fairly odd. And I think that's what made him."

The Pharmacist's Mate in his dispensary, World War II, in Arzou, Algeria

3

The Developing Therapist

Once in Los Angeles, Milton, like many young men of that era, tried his luck in the movie business, as a stuntman. And, as with so many others, the big break never came. He soon walked away from show business and returned to his first love – movement – and to the development of his sensitive hands. In fact, it was not show business alone that had attracted him to Los Angeles. In Florida, he had seen a magazine ad for the Berry Institute in Encino. Milton Berry, a well-known physical therapist of the day, was looking for young men who were interested in learning physical therapy.

At the Institute, it was Milton Berry, Junior who greeted him and promptly brushed him off. But what about the magazine ad, Milton wanted to know. "Forget it," said the rude son. "You'll never get to see the old man." Angry, Milton left. He was going to have to make his own way in this new town.

Back in Miami, outside of one brief romance, he had never paid much attention to girls; he was too much on the move to notice, too absorbed with the body and its dynamic expressions. In Los Angeles, however, through a cousin with whom he was living in Glendale, he met Marcella Levine, one of seven sisters in a lively and close-knit Jewish family, the patriarch of which had recently died. A pious man, like Milton's father, the elder Levine had worked as the sexton of a local synagogue. Milton became a frequent visitor in their home and gradually fell in love with Marcie.

She was the last daughter still living at home and the most unusual of the sisters. Slow to marry, she was indifferent to the typical men in her social set. But Milton was different from them and like her in important ways. Neither of them showed any interest in possessions or material wealth. Her sisters described them as ethereal, not of this planet. Marcie painted and sculpted in clay, but she was also keenly attuned to the body and spiritual pursuits. She practiced yoga faithfully and taught it to others, and she was a vegetarian. Both of them, despite their otherworldliness, or perhaps because of it, had a surprising strength of faith underneath their gentleness. The two of them merged completely. He committed himself fully to Marcie, even adopting her vegetarian diet. They became inseparable and soon were married in a small family ceremony.

One sister, Bobby, intrigued by Milton's special talent, encouraged him to develop it professionally. As the owner of a Hollywood beauty salon that catered to the town's elite, and in which Marcie also worked, she was well positioned to promote and find paying clients for Milton, who had never actively sought money for his therapy. He worked on the daughter of Ruth Bowes, a voice teacher whom the Levine family knew. The girl, afflicted with cerebral palsy, was making her family miserable. In his patient, positive way, Milton gradually was able to calm her, improve her ability to move about, and help her become more self-sufficient. He also taught movement and body awareness to Bowes' vocal students. Before long, his regular clients included Meredith Willson, Joe E. Brown, Pat O'Brien, and Jack Warner's wife, among other Hollywood notables. He frequently did his work in their homes. Most of his clients, however, were ordinary people who found him by word of mouth. Never at this time or in his future years would he advertise or promote himself, or need to, to attract people to him.

One celebrity client, Gus Edwards, a producer who had discovered Al Jolson, was to trigger a leap in Milton's developing comprehension of the connection between mind and body. Edwards had Parkinson's disease and frequently called on Milton to help him relax into sleep. He was so rigid that he was unable to shift his neck from side to side without moving his entire body. As they were walking one day, they stopped to watch a tennis game in progress. Milton noticed that as Edwards became absorbed by the steady back and forth movement of the ball, his neck gradually took up the movement until it was moving quite freely. He realized instantly that seemingly immutable physical limitations might be released when the mind was in a certain special state. And the same rhythmic motion that had become a part of his own therapeutic technique was somehow connected with the release of those blocks.

Milton quickly nestled into the Levine fold. As always, his primary social circle was the family. His warmth and gentleness, his patience and unremitting desire to find and bring forth the health and potential of each person endeared him to everyone. Within the extended family, he was known as Uncle Milton. Anyone with a twinge, a bad back, any kind of physical problem, sought him out or was quickly directed, "Go see Uncle Milt." They all knew he had magical hands, and they sent their friends and acquaintances for his help as well.

Before the marriage, he lived in a modest apartment in the Westlake Park area near downtown Los Angeles. He treated the famous and the ordinary while Marcie pursued her artistic interests. At the same time, he regularly taught movement classes at a gym, which he rented for that purpose. Calling his work "Rhythmic Harmonization," he used movements based on the exercises he had developed on the sand in Miami, movements designed to bring awareness and feeling into the body. In 1945, in an article in Physical Culture, his old hero Bernarr McFadden's magazine, he described the method this way:

> "It is like dancing – first you pause and listen to the music, then the rhythm within you pulsates to the rhythm of the music, your body begins swaying and before you realize it, you're on your feet dancing. But it doesn't have to be music for there is a rhythm to everything in life and if you will just get the "feel" of that rhythm, there are no limits to what your body will do."

The Levine family was the social center of Milton's life. Ben Light, composer of "Melancholy Baby" and other hit songs of the time, had married another Levine sister and frequently accompanied at the piano as Milton danced at family gatherings; he also played at Milton's wedding. Once married, Marcie and Milton moved close to Bobby and her husband in Manhattan Beach, south of Los Angeles, and lived happily, working and enjoying life with family and friends until the United States entered World War II.

In 1943 Milton, expecting to be drafted, decided to enlist in the Navy and was assigned to the medical corps. He employed his old therapeutic skills while still in boot camp in Idaho, helping his officers with their sore necks and backs. He was rewarded by a quick assignment out, although it was not where he had hoped to go. His orders took him to the Mediterranean, on board Landing Ship Tank 314, off the North Africa coast, where he helped run sick bay as a Pharmacist's Mate. Dr. Sven, the ship's doctor, had been a surgeon at the Mayo Clinic before the war. He discovered Milton's skills and soon had him showing the crew the exercises that he had taught for years in Miami and Los Angeles. Each day the enlisted men assembled on deck, stripped to the waist in the bright sun, as Milton demonstrated how to stand and walk comfortably and move without causing themselves injury. "Imagine a gang of cussing sailors going for my esthetic routines," he wrote in a letter to the Florida Traegers, signing off as, "your still lucky Milton Trager."

His letters to Miami downplayed the more frightening aspects of the war. He wrote of Italian allies bestowing crucifixes and religious pictures on him for delivery to their relatives in the United States. He described his efforts to learn to play a piano that was stowed near the ship's boiler room, as he sat stripped down and sweating in the hundred degree heat. And he spoke at length of a visit to a walled North African city, unnamed in the letter due to wartime censorship, where he was touched by the sincerity of the local Jewish population, which took him in like family, fed him, and showed him their synagogues. Atop the letter he added, "Mr. Censor, I am using some Hebrew words of religious significance in this letter."

In each letter home, he advised and encouraged his father, who was suffering with urinary incontinence after a surgery. He instructed him to use mind concentration to stop the flow, by remembering how it felt before the problem started in order to restimulate the neurological reflexes. He expressed sorrow at not being home to help him personally. And he reassured the family that he was under no strain and was relaxing and getting a tan under the Mediterranean sun. To his brother Dave, who at the time was in Coast Guard training in Groton, Connecticut, he wrote lightly, "So far I haven't fed the fishes. Been in a few raids but I've been the lucky brother you all claim I am." When he described the violent action more specifically, he still accented the positive; after several nights fighting off air raids during the Sicily campaign, he wrote, "The barrage of lead and steel thrown up by our guns keeps the dumb German buzzards too high for accuracy. I had to pinch hit on the gun the other night and got a big kick out of passing the stuff. It's fun to be in all of this, seeing our splendid equipment and well trained, toughened men going into battle."

In reality, the action at times tested his personal limits and forced him to doubt his choice of the medical corps, knowing that his fellows were actively fighting. His ship hit the beach in the first landing in Salerno, Italy. With shells bursting all around him, and the blood of the wounded and dead flowing out the scuppers, Milton, in a state of shock, found himself momentarily paralyzed, unconsciously holding onto a ship's cannon. It was nowhere in his previous experience, even in the boxing ring, nowhere in his character to be involved in such deadly violence and brutality. Finally, he pulled himself together, remembering, with a start, his responsibilities to the wounded men.

To his sister Sarah he wrote of the irony of his situation, after befriending an aerial gunner he had doctored. "In this case war and peace go hand in hand. When the hand with peace in it strengthens the body, it gives it back to war, and so it goes round and round, until war finally claims it forever."

It was in letters to Marcie, however, that he revealed something more of his conflict and pain, his need for her support and companionship, and their mutual dependence. She had been writing to him daily from Los Angeles; he felt her pain and loneliness and sought to teach her his way of coping with it.

"My darling, I just wish I could be behind the wheel of my own car, with you by my side, headed, who knows where."

"Every once in a while I find a little job to do, which pleases me very much, as I want to help in any way I can."

Describing a raid the previous night in a letter whose language he veiled to satisfy the censors, he told of personally "passing some mickeys" to the enemy.

"This was my most intimate contact with these ruffians who are keeping us and millions of others apart, and I am now satisfied that I can take it and help dish it out. You were of great help last night, my dearest one, and were ever by my side. I needn't feel ashamed and tell lies when the kids say, 'Uncle Milt, tell us about the war.' Not a scratch, and am much better for my experience.

I guess I shouldn't write letters like this my darling, but it can't be helped. Use the strength and stability you can obtain from me, like you gave me last night. It can be done, don't try to do it, just let it come to you...It's just very simple seeking, accepting and using."

He later was assigned to the U.S.S. Thomas Stone, which ultimately ran aground on a reef off Algiers. The sharp discrimination between officers and nonofficers on board rankled him, particularly as he was now under-the command of a captain who was universally feared and disliked by the enlisted men. Fortunately for Milton, the captain had a bad back and soon came to him for treatments. Once he relieved him of his chronic pain, Milton never had to worry about getting in trouble. The other men scrambled to look busy whenever the martinet captain came around, but when the skipper inspected Milton's area, he only ran an indifferent finger along the door to check for dust and then went his way. Other men also sought Milton's treatments during the war: crew members with aches and pains and others with disabilities found him and were helped; even visiting U.S. Senator Cabot Lodge received a treatment.

There was time too now to engage in other old pursuits. He entertained the crew with his singing and dancing and took on a boxing protegé, a young black welterweight whom he successfully coached and seconded in the ring. His pugilistic coaching made use of the knowledge he had developed in his therapeutic work. Writing home about the fighter, he said, "He showed his opponent that boxing isn't all physical."

In November of 1944, Milton telegrammed home. "I'M STILL LUCKY MOM TOMORROW CIVILIAN AGAIN LOVE." A series of asthma attacks had cut short his service obligation. He emerged from the Mediterranean war theater with three battle stars and a promotion to Pharmacist First Class, and he returned home to Los Angeles and Marcie, a decorated veteran, to resume his therapeutic practice. He and Marcie built, over the next two years, a combination home, art studio, and treatment facility in Tarzana, in the San Fernando Valley. A large sign on the front lawn advertised his specialty as rehabilitation of spastic and infantile paralysis. They lived contentedly while practicing their respective arts and were once again firmly ensconced in the Levine family fold, spending most weekends at the comfortable home of Bobbi and her husband.

It was at a party given to celebrate the opening of their office that Milton met a friend of the family, Emily Laser, who years later would become the next important woman in his life. Characteristically, he was drawn to her because of a physical problem. She had had trouble walking from the time she was a twelve-year-old girl in Sioux City, Iowa, and had been managed poorly by her doctors at the time. She had recently been confined to a wheelchair by her latest physician and had resigned herself to spending the rest of her life in it. In the midst of the festivities, Milton took her to his treatment room and began to work on her legs.

"What makes you think you have to walk in pain?" Milton asked.

Tears rolled down her cheeks, as relief that she had never experienced before began to flow into her damaged limbs. During this same period, Milton also treated a writer, Turnley Walker, who had been crippled for a year after a bout with polio and was desperate for help. Walker later wrote about that experience.

"I heard of Trager, grudgingly, through a local medical doctor and on this sun-baking afternoon drove to his small building in my car with its hand-operated controls. On my high metal crutches, one leg locked stiff in the long brace and the other half-braced, I struggle up the curving walk to the porch of the building. Above me the door opens. A compact, easy-moving man steps out on the porch. This is Milton Trager. His blue eyes hold mine, then run down over my body, finding instantly where the weakness starts in my hips and slides its tyranny downward to my braced, helpless feet.

"'Polio,' he says.

'I came to see you,' I say, hearing my voice harden, meaning to let him know that I expect little or nothing.

He smiles gently down. He has missed nothing in my expression and the tone of my voice, but he smiles, his eyes crinkling, a glowing in his blue eyes that seems almost love. I do not understand.

Through an archway and then I lower myself with wrenching effort into a chair. He sits at his desk across from me, relaxed, leaning on his arms stretched out easily on the desk top, leaning without pressure, his back lithely bowed, the freckled forearms powerful but not thick, a gracefully strong man. His shoulders bunch up the white open-throated shortsleeved shirt. He smiles at me gently.

'Nothing much wrong from the waist up,' he says. 'But the gluteals and on down from there...' A soft hand gesture illustrates strength fading out. 'The left leg mainly, but the left foot is stronger than the right, although the right leg is better.'

I stare at him, wondering where he has seen my muscle chart, knowing he has not.

'I might be able to help you,' he says.

He has two rooms where he gives his treatments. One is spacious with an expanse of open floor, for walking, balancing, special exercises. The other is a cubicle with barely enough space around the treating table for his necessary movements when he is working on a patient.

'I want us to fit in here good and tight,' he tells me. 'I don't want to lose any pressure.'

Trager has learned to press all of his physical and mental energy on the precise points where greatest stimulation is possible. Raw strength is never used. Often when his efforts are greatest and most concentrated, his hands – his fingers – will touch me most lightly. Sweat will wash his face and shoulders. And yet there will be only a lightly vibrating pressure from his thumb and forefinger.

He has given me balance! I don't know how he has done this. It seems to have come all at once. I am in the big room, moving around much more easily than before – my God, moving. If I could ever explain to anyone what that means!

'Hey, look at this,' I announce.

'Why not?' he smiles, with that little shrug of his, moving himself, always moving with me. I have the idea that the sense of really moving has come to me from inside him, some sort of half-weird transfer he has arranged.

He is in front of me and he has taken away – when? – the Canadian canes I am using now. He is touching me, or is he? It can't be with more than his fingertips and he is speaking to me very softly, about balance – balancing – I don't remember the words. Maybe there are no words, just the idea. I am looking at him, into his eyes, and I am balancing.

'Hey!' I laugh.

'Why not?' he says softly, with the little shrug...

I climb the front steps by myself.

'How about that?' I demand.

He shrugs but his eyes are glowing."

While he rarely spoke of his war experiences, Milton had been deeply affected, and he returned home with a new internal resolve. Though his practice flourished and he was helping people with everything from spastic paralysis to bad backs and sore necks, he had no license to perform his art. Slowly, encouraged by his California family, he began the painstaking process of filling in the gaps in his learning and developing a career.

At the time, the state was licensing a category of personnel known as Drugless Practitioners who could engage in all elements of medicine except surgery and the prescribing of medications. An earlier group of practitioners called Naturopaths had been grandfathered into this newer designation. Milton now enrolled in the Los Angeles College of Drugless Physicians and began his studies, eventually gaining licensure from the state. He still felt unsatisfied and incomplete, however. He knew that his way of working with the body was effective, that his personal discoveries had value, but he understood, too, that they would never go further unless he could persuade doctors to adopt them. Neither doctors nor established physical therapists accepted the ideas behind his work; they did not consider him to be a legitimate therapist. Frustrated, and badly wanting acceptance, he realized that doctors would never listen to him unless he had the proper credentials.

Thus he decided, at age 42, to go to medical school. As with all his endeavors, he plunged in wholeheartedly, sending applications to all the medical schools in the United States except the medical college for women. Not one of them wanted a man his age and certainly not a man with such an irregular personal and academic background.

Undaunted, Milton decided to explore the next closest country: Mexico. He enrolled in a high school Spanish class and attended three nights a week after work. He soon realized, however, that hours of "how are you?" and "John and Mary are going home" were not going to get him very far in medical school. Impulsively, he decided to lease the house, gather up his remaining veteran's benefits, and head south with Marcie, with just a few of their belongings jammed into his car. There was a medical school in Guadalajara, and a teacher of Marcie's who lived there had offered to help him get started. The climate was good, the city was reputed to be beautiful, so off they went to learn the language where it was spoken.

His patient, Turnley Walker, with whom he had grown quite close by then, wrote of their last meeting before the departure.

"'I will be all right,' he tells me.

"I get up much more easily than was possible before I found him. We shake hands.

"'It's what I've got to do.'

"I leave his doorway and reach my car in his driveway. I turn back. He waves to me from the porch, and then stands there in his white trousers and white shortsleeved shirt, relaxed, slouching and steady, his head with its fringe of reddish hair held out a little, the manly, battered face with its merciful and forever undefeated expression."

Photographer's model

Who can land the softest?

4

What Is Soft?

Sheila Merle Johnson glides quickly, efficiently around the Best Western meeting room, preparing the class for Milton's arrival. She is tall and thin with a dancer's long legs. Curly blonde hair frames a bright and active face. Milton picked her early as an instructor; she is popular with students, and her fluent French makes her a sought-after teacher in Europe. Today she begins coordinating the six-day Reflex Response class in Laguna Hills, hoping to coax words out of Milton to explain his way of working.

As usual in this special class, the students are all experienced practitioners, developed enough in their skills to work with people that have serious medical conditions. Jim and Carol Day have flown in from New Jersey, Sally Nye from Massachusetts. Amrita Daigle and Michel Van Waeyenberge, who speak English haltingly, come from French-speaking Quebec. Most of the other students live in the Western states. The assistants and logistics people are also veteran practitioners who donate their time out of commitment to the work but who also relish the chance to spend more time with Milton, to observe the dramatic effects of his subtle labors and to better grasp the Reflex Response work. There is much to do; from the second day of training on, two shifts of people per day with serious medical problems will be coming to be models.

Milton and Emily arrive. All the bustle stops when they walk through the door. Her movement is limited today; she uses a walker to get around, the result of unsuccessful surgery for a broken hip. He looks serious, almost morose, his craggy brows knitted, his cheeks deeply furrowed. Everyone gathers for the opening circle; one by one the practitioners speak of their expectations for the class and their reasons for coming. These usually confident men and women act nervous; they are excited and anxious and happy and confused at the same time. No matter their successes at home, they are only novices in Milton's presence, especially in this area of his work. He downplays his abilities: "I've just been at it longer," he says, feeling their uncertainty and intuitively working to bolster their confidence.

He sits, quiet and receptive, listening to each student and assistant in the circle, feeling more than hearing their words. He breaks in to say something once he senses their particular needs, or he silently nods an acknowledgement. Today, the first day of class, the students will practice Reflex Response techniques on one another. Tomorrow the models will arrive; they have been recruited into the workshop by practitioners. They are attracted, like the students, by the chance to be touched by the master.

In the following days, there will be several models with cerebral palsy, two adults and two children. Milton talks about his own formative work on a child with cerebral palsy when he first arrived in Los Angeles in 1937. The daughter of a voice teacher, the girl was a holy terror when Milton first started with her. She yelled, threw her food, could hardly move around, and made life miserable for her family. As an untrained therapist, he worked with her three times a week for eight years; by the end of treatment, she was calm and could get around and take care of herself. He tells the students that he learned more from working with her than from any other of his patients.

Now the students are busy arranging tables for the practice session. They pair up and begin their usual work; he watches, moving from one table to the next. At each table he comments on the students' work or moves them aside with a wave of his hand and demonstrates his way. Sometimes he has the student cover his hands with theirs as he works, so they can feel the difference. If that is not enough, he says,"Hang onto my neck; lay on me." His words are abrupt, brief, cryptic, and sharp today.

Feel your way in. As you touch the body say, 'well hello
there. Ohhh....'?

I'm getting acquainted with the tissue. Not everyone is
the same.
I want you all to learn body weight better. Feel your
weight coming in.
All tension is in the midline. Work away from the midline.
Your hands are dumb. Know it's the mind you're after,
not the tissue.
Step out of the picture, you personally. It's not you. You
shouldn't have to decide what to do. Feel it. When you
are too fast, feel the weight; it will slow you down.
From feeling now. Go.
Too much hurry. I want you to saunter around the table.

Suddenly aware of his brusqueness, feeling a reaction from one of
the students, he says,"If I'm abrupt, don't mind me," then he continues on. When he sees another student getting it just right, he shouts
out emphatically, "I'll buy it!"

Now he begins to talk specifically about the Reflex Response work,
how it evokes responses from paralyzed, weak, lifeless tissue. "You
have to learn to tease the muscles," he says. He lifts the bare leg of a
student lying supine on a table, bending it slightly at the knee and
seeming to steadily push it into her hip as he searches for just the
right position. The other students, intently observing but perplexed,
have no idea what makes one position right and not another. He
explains what he is doing, at much greater length than normal.

"The leg is neither here nor there. I won't let her go this way or
that way – it's aggravating. I'm resisting but it gives her the feeling
that she's resisting. I don't want her to know anything." Then, to the
student on the table who is experiencing this sensation, "I don't have
you and you don't have me." The key, he says, is not to overpower
muscles that are already extremely weak. They must first develop a
minimal response; it teaches them how much strength is needed.
"All I want is a reflex, not a big 'schmeer,' because if there's great
force, they don't need you; they're not paralyzed. We're in the habit
of making things happen. Not in this work."

The students ask questions as he comes to the table where they work, and Sheila Merle pushes him to describe, explain, break down what he does. Milton either does not understand what they want or cannot explain it better than he has already done. His answers grow shorter, more defensive, and inflexible; he is clearly irritated at Sheila Merle, who is only trying to coax words out of him for the students' benefit.

He demonstrates his soft receptive attitude toward the body for another student. "I'm opening myself to find out what's wrong with, 'Well...?'" As he stretches out the word, his face turns upward with a questioning look. "I don't dive into the move." Then, emphatically, "The patient must win." He sees another student who has the feeling. "Now, dammit!, you're doing it right. You're conditioning the unconscious mind." It is a curse of approval, which forcefully encourages the student and burns itself into his memory.

There are more questions, more prodding by Sheila Merle. Milton is frustrated; so are the students, but they do not blame him for it. In the end, he apologizes. "Forgive me for not being bright, for not being what I'm supposed to be – I need a body with a problem in front of me. It's not something that can be taught; it has to be learned."

Day two starts with another circle. Milton is lighter this time; he reminisces about his Navy years, telling how he got out of binds by helping people with his work. His face lights up at the memories as he sits comfortably in his white, short-sleeved shirt and slacks, Emily by his side. The models enter, go to their tables, and meet the practitioners who will work with them. Milton makes his rounds, getting a little medical history from each person, but he evaluates them mainly by observing and putting his hands on their bodies, moving them. "I get acquainted first with the tissue," he explains.

The first model, a woman in her thirties, has long standing spasticity and weakness in her legs. She wears braces and points her right leg to the side when she walks, jerking and landing heavily on the other leg. Milton has her remove her braces and pants; he watches her walk away from him and toward him. "Let's get rid of that lurch to the right," he says. "Boom, toom, boom," he imitates the unnecessary force of each step toward the right. "I'll be happy to leave it here," she retorts.

"Let's do a silly thing," Milton coaxes. "Pretend your feet are round. They're round." His voice is soft, like a muffled sob; each phrase seems to be surrendered up. The woman walks again; this time her movement is smoother, less forced. He has her lie down on the table and begins to move her flaccid legs, developing resistance, working and talking simultaneously. He announces to the students that she needs to strengthen her abductor muscles and hip flexors, to develop muscle action in her left leg by means of resistance work. He speaks to the woman, to the students, to himself:

> This is the bad leg, this is the good one.
> You have to learn to feel the difference.
> My object in life is to develop more sensitive therapists.
> Excuse me for calling it a 'bad' leg.
> Is Emily clear to see?
> Emily smiles and nods her head...You think I'm running the show?
> I'm satisfied.
> There! We're together. Thank you!
> Oh dammit! I wish I had a wire hooked onto my head into your brain. [The students titter. "Me too."]
> I'm using three pounds pressure. She's the boss. You develop your intensity, as if you were her.
> There! You came in! Solid! Thank you! Thank you very much! I feel you! I love it! I like your smile, I love it, you've made my day.
> It has to start in the unconscious mind.

Milton brings in a practitioner to work with her and slowly moves to another table where a sixty-two-year-old man sits who had polio thirty years earlier. His left leg is atrophied; he drags it along as he walks, raising that hip high each time. He also has tremors in his upper body, and pain and sensitivity in his hands and feet from Guillain-Barre syndrome, a neurological disease that sometimes follows a viral illness. He is thin, with a whitening beard and long, straight hair. He wears a leg brace and uses a tall staff to help him walk. Milton has him walk, tells him to move as though he is leading with his left hip. Immediately, there is less dragging of that leg. He has the man stand and shows him his balance point, instructing him to practice balancing many moments daily.

On to the next table, where a forty-six-year-old woman who sustained an auto accident six years earlier is paralyzed from the mid-back down. Milton gets her practitioner onto the table and demonstrates how to work with the patient on all fours, establishing balance and developing strength. With the model supine on the table, he feels her thin, lifeless legs. To raise her leg so that the knee is bent and the foot rests on the table, the woman grabs folds of loose skin on her thigh and drags her right leg up. The leg flops over to the side. He balances it, using the lightest touch of his fingers.

"That's where you start. Balance felt like......? I feel heaviness; a heavy leg. We have to bring a sense of lightness," Milton says. He gradually, gently starts his resistance work, waiting for a response. "You are giving her the feeling of abduction. There, I felt a waver! You gave me a little nothing. Thank you! Thank you, dammit!"

The last model of the morning is a fifty-three-year-old woman with recently diagnosed amyotrophic lateral sclerosis, Lou Gehrig's disease. She has had two hip replacements and has a chronically displaced left shoulder. She keeps the arm on that side immobilized against her torso with a sling. Milton begins to feel her, to work with her. No condition surprises him or daunts him. For him, the potential for change, for improvement, is unconditionally available for every person. "No hay problema," he says to an assistant who speaks Spanish. No problem. Milton feels good, and Sheila Merle, coordinating the workshop with her typical skill, has given up on getting more out of Milton than he is able or willing to give.

That afternoon and the next day more patients come. A young woman who sustained a head injury is weakened on the right side. She has double vision, reduced mobility, and balance problems. Milton says she must learn the degree of lightness and the degree of strength needed to function. A woman with multiple sclerosis and rheumatoid arthritis has back, leg, and bladder spasms. A sixty-year-old man has cerebral palsy and also had polio at age sixteen. His wife is there too, also with cerebral palsy; she is confined to a motorized wheelchair. There is another post-polio woman with severe weakness, a post-polio man, a man with right-sided weakness from a stroke, and a woman with left-sided paralysis, also from a stroke. A ten-year-old boy and a two-year-old girl have cerebral palsy; neither one can walk unassisted. And an eighty-year-old woman's knee and hip chronically buckle from weakness.

Milton gets acquainted with each individual, through words and touch. The words are soft at first, passively questioning, receptive, until he gets a feel for the person. As he begins his work with each person, no matter what happens or how far he advances, he always embeds the notion that this is just the beginning. He does not predict exactly how much change and progress are possible, only that they are possible. Each time he makes his rounds, he deepens the feeling connection with the person, whether student or patient. His voice softens; he emanates tenderness and surrender, love and a kind of confident resignation with each word.

> You're beautiful.
> I love your face.
> Yes, darling.
> Lay down.
> Come, talk.

A patient looks up at him after he has worked with her a moment, her eyes glistening with love and gratitude. "He knows what I am feeling," she says to her practitioner. Yet when he works with the forty-year-old man with polio, intending to build strength in his weakened leg, another mood bursts forth. He is doing resistance work, forcing the man to push against his subtly gradated pressure. His words are rough, intense, explosive.

"Push me down! Slam me! Slam me, dammit! Bang me! Let me have it! That's it! I want you to get *the feeling, the feeling* of what is strong. Fight me! Don't let me go away! I don't feel you, let me feel you! I feel you better." (Then softly, "You okay, Emily?"). Dammit go! That's what I want! That's you. I'll buy it. That's wonderful. I want you like that all over the place. That's not enough! That's enough! Just let me have you; you have nothing to do with it." And to the student standing close by, "When they get the feeling they are doing it, you are reaching the unconscious mind. Until you do that, you are not doing anything."

He works briefly with the paraplegic woman and speaks to her, to her mind, when her leg muscles respond . "Thank you, you're there! You're there waiting for me!" She feels the new energy rippling in her legs and smiles broadly. He returns to the withered leg of the bearded man with Guillain-Barre. "I felt a more alive feeling, a more solid feeling. We've broken through the pattern." To the student, "What he needs desperately is to get the waver out of him. You are to ask, gently, 'Well....? What am I going to do about that...?'"

He moves to the paralyzed legs of the woman with polio, helping her balance them unaided as she lies on the table, adding a feathery touch only when the leg drifts out of balance. "Just start with a thought. Don't try to do it. Just a hair. Hey, it's doing all kinds of stuff now! Just teasing it. That's enough; thank you. Then come back to a feeling of balance." Once again he returns to the man with Guillain-Barre, taking over for a moment from the student. He likes what he's feeling, a readiness of the weakened leg muscles to respond. "Dammit yes! He's in there, he's punchy, he's ready to get me. Don't let me! Thank you! I felt you then." Now he is back again to the woman, working the paralyzed legs: "I feel something going now. I don't know what it is. Now you're coming into it. Now you're stronger. I'm feeling all kinds of stuff. Ah. Thank you. Dammit. There it is. You're there with me now."

Milton is pleased with the work today. His memory drifts back to another paralyzed leg, to the first child with polio he worked with, back in Miami when he was still a teenager himself. He remembers the first moment of change: "I felt a flicker, no more than that. Then more than a flicker, then it moved." He tells the students standing around him today, more than sixty years later, "There is so much intensity between the practitioner and patient that a reaction happens." When a student wants more information, asking, "Do you want to bring tonus into the tissue?" his answer is vague. "No, it's just something I want to do." The students will have to learn on their own, using their memory to recapture the extraordinary events of the day.

The next day's work is equally good; Milton is all business, very serious and rather short with his students. He works on the couple with cerebral palsy, attending not only to their spastic muscles but also to their voices. He grasps the skin under the man's lower jaw lightly and shimmers it as he has him repeat words: "hello, how are you, what is your name, Monday, Tuesday, Wednesday." He is keeping the throat muscles from grabbing and squeezing after each word, allowing the breath from the abdomen to do the work. The man laughs and smiles as he hears his own voice relaxing, the sounds lengthening and becoming intelligible.

The woman's lower jaw is severely displaced to the left. Milton is unhappy with this. He can't resist addressing this before doing vocal work with her. He takes the jaw firmly into his hand and gently rocks her entire head with it. He lets it rest and starts again. Slowly, gradually the mandible loosens, and the large, distorted gap between the jaws diminishes. He asks her frequently, sweetly, "Am I hurting you?" and doesn't quite believe her denials. He eyes her with doubt. Students are observing with silent amazement. After three or four minutes, she looks almost normal and is laughing with glee. He does no Reflex Response work on the spastic muscles of the palsied couple. With them he imparts a thousand times the feeling of softness until their muscles begin to loosen.

His teaching today is pure simplicity. After a piece of successful work, he says, "I like it. I like the feeling. I'm learning all the time; this is new to me. I want deeper projection of what is soft." He tells the models, "I don't teach my students. They pick up the feeling of what makes me tick. When you pick a Trager practitioner, choose them for their projection of softness."

He works on the unbending rigidity of a man with Parkinson's

Disease, the husband of a practitioner. She stands and watches intently, knowing how severe her man's condition is and wanting badly to learn better ways of working with him. Milton sits astride the table, near the man's head. His own head is thrown back slightly, his eyes closed as he works with the deepest possible concentration. It is as though he is travelling a great distance inside to reach the damaged unconscious mind of this very ill man. He brings a bit more movement into the stiff neck and silently leaves. He can do no more here.

Now he moves casually to the table where a two-year-old girl with cerebral palsy sits with her hopeful mother. Milton's every movement with her is the essence of gentleness and sweetness. The girl doesn't flinch or withdraw as this old stranger touches her. Her legs are weak. He smoothes them caressingly then lifts a foot. He allows her to retract her toes from his hand, which holds them. He has brought her leg muscles into activity without stimulating spasticity, as easily as that. "I'll take what she gives me," he says with a shrug. "The patient has to win." He tells the mother to touch the child in this soft way, each time she passes her. When the woman reveals how physical therapists have been working with the girl, he grows angry. He complains that they haven't changed in years and predicts that his work will replace their manipulations in a few years. Emily is nearby, watching him with concern.

The final workshop day, Milton stresses Mentastic® movements, which he teaches patients and which he has used in this training to help the models bring back the feeling of their improved state. "You have to invent Mentastics for the individual. Be creative. Become so fluid that you can feel them within yourself first. You're to recall and recall and recall. Just the thought of it. No big thing." With models and students alike, he is intimate but at the same time objective, even impersonal.

Again today there is a child with cerebral palsy, a nine-year-old boy with beautifully tender and intelligent eyes, who uses leg braces and a walker, or a wheelchair, to get around.

Every move he makes, every word he uses builds the child's trust and reinforces softness in his spastic muscles. Milton can not impart this skill directly to students; it has grown out of long years of experience with children. "I want to teach you what softness is. Here, feel my arm. That's soft. All of these people are my students, nice people, my friends. I'm just going to see how soft your neck is, how soft, how nothing," he says. "Nothing's going to happen. You can believe me." The child trusts him instantly.

"I like the softness you're giving me. I like it. I like your soft touch on my thumb," Milton says as the boy's arm, at first retracted toward his head, gradually stretches out and relaxes. "What is soft?" he asks as always. To the boy this is a novel question. "What is soft?" the boy repeats, wonderingly. "What is softer than that?" asks Milton. "What is softer than that?" echoes the child, with surprised curiosity. He gives the boy images to use: being soft is sweet, like ice cream; being tight and hard is sour, like a dill pickle. Milton flexes and moves the child's legs slowly and with infinite patience. There is not a hurried movement or word. The palsied legs, scissored at the knees, steadily soften and increase their range of motion under his hands. If the slightest spastic reaction develops, he backs off immediately but unhurriedly. Milton addresses the students. "He doesn't like that movement; it causes spasticity, so I won't do it. I'll do what I can get away with, not a speck more. You have to breathe with them, get inside them. I feel like I am inside them."

The students ask questions. They want more information, more guidance. But Milton's guidance often takes forms they do not expect. Patiently he demonstrates, watches, throws out a phrase capturing the feeling he has picked up rather than analyzing a particular movement. He struggles to make the students feel what he feels. When they verbalize their questions, he often cuts them off and answers quickly. His assessment and response are also quick, and they frequently leave people perplexed. Each time he leaves students with a model he has just worked on, they struggle to emulate him, to feel his feeling. Sometimes they succeed, sometimes they remain confused or frustrated. Their caring communicates with the models nonetheless, and the same intimate bonds that Milton creates with his patients also form between his students and these models. With the models Milton is always solicitous, but with them too, he sometimes fails to accurately hear or understand their comments. Yet he quickly apologizes for his shortcomings when he becomes aware of them. He works too long on one woman, causing her back to go into spasm. "I got too ambitious," he says. "Take away one of the good marks you gave me."

At the next table, the practitioner says that the woman she is working with has a frontal headache. The pain seems to have moved up her body and lodged in her head. The model says the pain is coming from a physical release of tension. Eyes closed, her face bespeaks suffering. Milton tells the practitioner he would work at her temples and on her neck. It's a cycle or pattern that must be broken. "I don't know where to start," he says. "I'll just start. Do I bother you?" She tells him that it is more than a physical pain, but his attention is elsewhere at the moment. When he realizes she's talking to him, he apologizes for his poor hearing. "I'll talk louder," she replies. "Not too loud," he deadpans. "Then everyone will know I'm hard of hearing."

The woman breaks into laughter and announces that her headache is gone. "Not already!", Milton says in mock horror. "I'm not that good! It happened." The shared humor has created a powerful intimacy. "Bless you," the woman says. "Bless you," he answers. "The continuity was broken, the pattern block. What's important is the recall, including the humor. You'll become master of that pain. That's what I want."

"The pain is a lot more than physical, I hope you realize that," the woman says.

"Who do you think I am?!" Milton says loudly, with mock outrage, having said thousands of times during his lifetime that it is not the body, but the mind that controls the body.

"God?" she offers in grateful response.

"Noooooo," he says hopelessly. He hates being a guru and tells the story of a girl he helped in Mexico, and the priest's concerned admonition to him: 'first God, Milton; then you.' He looks at the woman. The feeling between them is strong and loving.

"I thank you for what you have told me. I take nothing for granted. Nothing. If you have the feeling of nothingness, you can't have pain. Thank you for letting me. That's why I need more years to live. There's so much out there."

The day's models are about to leave, and the workshop's closing circle about to begin. Some of the models describe their experience.

"I'm feeling my body right now. It really feels there."

"I feel like I'm moving a lot different than I did two or three days ago.

Milton replies, "It's only the beginning."

"I've never seen her stand this long on her own," says the mother of the baby with cerebral palsy.

"I think it's always good to do something for yourself," says a woman who appreciated the movement training she has received. Another woman thanks Milton for having taught her practitioner, who has made such a big difference in her life.

Once the models have gone, the students, instructors, and assistants gather together. The room darkens in the November late afternoon. Milton sits at ease, looking husky and strong in his white clothes. As he addresses the group, his phrases drift farther and farther apart, the words spilling out ever more slowly.

"You're fortunate to have had the boy with cerebral palsy. You've changed as a result. The degree of softness needed has taught you. That's what I want – for you to look forward to getting these more difficult problems, not get scared off, wondering instead, 'What should I do?' But don't try to get these people; be open to receive them."

A practitioner who appreciated Milton's sweet and sour image for the spastic boy notes that, in French, the same word – doux – is used for 'sweet' and 'soft'."How could I be that lucky?" Milton says. Another practitioner says he was helped by working with a model who had great pain, because he has always been so fearful of causing pain.

"If you're honestly there, they pick it up," Milton responds, then goes on. "You have to go through the same process I did. I'm just out there longer. I'm not this good; I'm just hooked up this good." He slowly raises his arms from his lap and spreads them in a gesture of surrender and openness. The dusk deepens inside the quiet, unlit room. The words fall from his mouth one by one. Everyone present is drawn into the profound peaceful feeling that Milton is creating out of his own unconscious.

"I've learned how to work with myself......the step beyond.....oh, I can do that...I'm still out of it....that's where I want you.....you are to ask......Well..?.... humm..?....solid.......when the two of you are there....not special...you've lost it then....Well..?....There's nothing to be done about it....It is this simple........"

Trying to keep his head above water in his 4th year medical school clinical class, Guadalajara, Mexico, 1953

5

"Primero Dios, Segundo Tu"

"We went to a hotel in the central part of Guadalajara, and the very next morning I went to the medical school with great determination plus an attitude of 'what the hell, they can't shoot you for wanting to go to school.' I walked around the patio reading various signs over doors until I came to one that read 'Director.' Luckily for me it is spelled the same in both languages. As I walked into this office, a substantial looking man came toward me on his way out. I surprised myself by saying 'Buenos días' and quickly started talking in my Spanish, hoping I was telling him that I wanted to enter. medical school. He, of course, didn't get that message, and he made some kind of motion that seemed to me like he was politely telling me to leave. He took off in a hurry, so I left.

"I had been rejected so many times in my trying to get into schools that it was natural to feel that it had happened again. Back at the hotel, my wife was waiting anxiously to hear what had happened. It was to be a whole new life for both of us here in Mexico, and it all depended upon whether or not I could get into this school. She asked, 'How did you make out? Can you get in here?'

"My unhappy answer was 'I don't know what really happened. I did not understand him and he very likely did not understand me. But I am going back to try again tomorrow.'

"Expecting nothing I went back to the same building the next morning. There I encountered the same man, and this time I used my other greeting: '¿Cómo está usted?' He said something, and with a smile, he took me by my shoulders and pushed me down into a chair. His next polite gesture came through to me positively, that I was to stay there. He then went out to the patio and it was clear that he was looking for an interpreter. In a few minutes, he came back with a nice-looking, neat young man with a mustache, who looked to be in his early twenties. When he said, in perfect stateside English, 'What can I do for you?' I could have hugged him. At last there was communication!

I blurted out, 'I want to go to medical school!' He translated this for the other man, who was the Dean of Medicine, Dr. Rubalcava, and who was obviously pleased that we had finally gotten together.

He answered in Spanish, 'Take him to the office and register him.'"

In this way Milton began the next phase in his life, six years in Mexico to train as a doctor. It was April; school started in mid-September. He and Marcella rented an apartment downtown, bought furniture, and set up housekeeping, while Milton tried to read books and newspapers to bolster his meager Spanish. He ultimately made bigger leaps in learning by hanging around school each day, playing poker with the interns and tossing coins against a wall with the freshmen. He began to absorb the feel and sound of the language, although in this informal environment he also picked up some choice extra words not found in any medical text.

"Several of the boys took a liking to me, maybe because I was a curiosity to them, as I was the only American in the school and old enough to be father to them. They became interested in teaching me their language. Soon they even had me conjugating verbs. When they took me to their friends so I could show off what I had learned, there was much hilarity. I knew then that I could not go into polite society using my new vocabulary. How far can you go with 'I have sex, you have sex, they have sex?'"

Once enrolled, Milton found himself swamped with hefty medical texts, some of them translated from French into Spanish. He was not only studying his medical subjects but also simultaneously preparing for more than twenty exams to complete his Bachelor of Science degree, which he received in 1949. While Marcie painted and sympathetically supported her husband's struggle, he studied half the night each night to prepare for the next day's class. There he had an equally difficult challenge. One professor spoke with a fat cigar in his mouth and was unintelligible to the American. Another professor spoke a mile a minute. Yet another didn't wear his false teeth; that was the worst. Now Milton lost even more sleep making up nightly what he had missed in class during the day.

Adding insult to injury, his classmates tittered every time the class roll was called and his name pronounced. Using the Spanish system, they had added his mother's family name – Cohen – to his surname; in Spanish that sounded like the word for 'they screw.' Angry now, Milton rushed to the registrar and changed the spelling of the name, and therefore the pronunciation, to put an end to this added humiliation.

The professors traditionally gave oral examinations, sitting in tribunal with two of their colleagues. Students paced the courtyard before an exam, waiting their turn nervously. Another student, Florita, pushed to the limit by her anxiety, dropped to one knee and made the sign of the cross. She pleaded with Milton not to tell her pious Jewish father what she had done.

For Milton the exams were literally a gamble. He had to pick a poker chip with a number on it out of a pile on the table; the number corresponded to a single question, the answer to which meant either success or failure for an entire course. Used to carrying a blackboard and chalk with him everywhere for help when his Spanish failed him, Milton drew pictures and acted out the parts, drawing on every resource in order to pass his courses.

"One examination stands out in my mind. It was in the class of Gynecology in my fourth year. It was the last exam I had to take that year, and I had expressed a desire to have it over with as soon as possible so I could leave for my home in California. The professor was giving a special lecture that day and the material was not part of the exam. When he concluded, he said, 'Miltone,' (that's how everyone pronounced my name) 'I will now give you your exam.'

I was not very happy about this, for my classmates had not been dismissed. As I looked around at the class, the professor spoke up. 'Don't mind if they stay – we are all your friends, Miltone.' I was stuck with it.

He gave me my question, which luckily I could talk about quite freely. I was really going quite well and I was enjoying the audience. Having been in show business, talking and acting before an audience was really exhilarating and did not bother me in the least after I got going on my subject. All of a sudden I needed a word, and I seemed to reach up in the air and grab something that I threw into my mouth and spit out as my answer. Now, the same word kept coming quite often in my discourse. It seemed to me that it was the right word, but every time I used it my friends laughed – not a polite titter or giggle. Their laughter became more hilarious and I was getting madder with every outburst. Even the maestro was smiling, but he encouraged me to continue. I had to keep on, as this exam was very important. I was relieved when the maestro said, 'Enough, Miltone, you have done well.' I thanked him and went toward the exit, and I was really burning.

I caught my good friend Sergio by the arm and propelled him out into the patio, making use of all the profanity in English and Spanish I could get out to relieve myself. Sergio was still amused, and this hurt me. I said, 'not you too, Sergio.' I didn't know whether to hit him or walk away as he took hold of both my arms and, with tears of laughter rolling down his cheeks, said, 'Milt, they were really not at fault. We are all your friends, believe me. But what can you expect when you insisted on using that same word over and over again? What you were saying was 'shit.'"

In his freshman year, his classmates invited him to join their soccer team. Although he had never played and the others had been kicking the ball almost since infancy, Milton couldn't resist the chance to use his athletic skills again. The girls in the class had made up the uniforms out of old flimsy shirt material, dying them a bright orange. They sewed identifying nicknames on the tops. One player's uniform said Perro – dog. Others spelled out masculine names like "Toro" – bull – or "Gallo" – rooster. Milton's said "Chapas," a word he didn't recognize. He knew it was a joke and went to one of his professors to get the word translated. With a laugh, the maestro informed him that it meant a man so decrepit that he has no teeth and can only gum his tortillas, a reference to Milton's advanced age compared to the other students.

Also in his first year, Milton was able to put his special abilities to use once again. Word had gotten out, before classes began, that he had experience working with children suffering from infantile paralysis. One day, while on break with the other students in the patio, a school official summoned him. He was brought into a consultation room. There, motionless on an examination table, lay a four-year-old girl, surrounded by the top medical school professors, several nuns, and a priest. Each of the professors had already examined the child and confirmed that her legs were totally paralyzed.

"Milton, aquí está una muchachita con parálisis infantil total." They pointed to the little girl with polio. Then they asked him to demonstrate his work. He began, as he had done so many times before. At first nothing, no response. Milton felt the lifeless tissues of her legs, touching them lightly, waiting, and knowing what he was waiting for. His fingers were sensing as they touched the leg; they were vibrating with feeling, giving the impression of movement, of life, opening new connections in the child's mind. His concentration was total, as the professors faded from his consciousness. Then it came: a response, the smallest twitter of a reflex response.

"¡Aquí está el reflejo!" There it is, a reflex! Only he perceived it at first, but as he continued working, the reflex gathered strength until finally the legs moved visibly. The priest and nuns dropped to the floor, fervently crossing themselves. The professors exchanged significant looks.

"¡Hay movimiento en las piernas!" The legs are moving!

"This child will walk," Milton asserted with confidence.

"We have an epidemic of polio here. You will do this work for us," a professor said definitively to the freshman. With a typical shrug, Milton assented.

The priest, visibly moved, grabbed him and pushed him back out into the courtyard. He took Milton by the shoulders, squared him around till they faced each other, and stared at him sternly.

"Tu trabajo es magnífico, Milton, pero.." Your work is magnificent, but remember.."primero Dios, segundo tu.." First God, then you.

"I agree with you," said Milton, marvelling at his strange situation as a Jewish man in this all Catholic school.

That child did walk, in three weeks' time, and Milton continued to see six to eight similar children each week, some of them coming from great distances, beginning that first year in school until he finished his medical studies; he earned a few extra pesos in the process. On one such occasion, as he sought to explain his work to the father of a ten-year-old girl, he used a phrase, in Spanish, that he would continue to employ throughout his career.

"Los músculos son tontos"—the muscles are dumb. He was emphasizing that the muscles only do the mind's bidding, that the mind must be reached, through feeling, to produce a change in the muscles which move the body and hold it together.

Milton fell in love with Mexico and its people; he admired their ingenuity in making do with the little they had, their earthy simplicity, which he shared in many ways, and their hard work. He impressed visitors from home with how perfectly he had adopted the customs, gestures, and language of his temporary home. He liked it that, to the Mexicans, everyone was family. He felt at home there. And the general poverty and scarcity of services ensured that the medical students would gain as much experience as they could handle, and more. That basic and practical training was to serve Milton well in future years, as was the siesta, a custom which he found to be very civilized. Many memorable incidents colored these training years. In his fifth year, while on the obstetrics service, he lived in the hospital a week at a time. Typically, a small boy would appear at the door and announce, "My mother is ready." Years later, Milton remembered one such occasion.

"With my partner, who was one year ahead of me in school, called my Jefe (Chief), we took off. This particular Jefe had to become a great doctor. He was raised on a farm, very poor, squat of build with shoulders as broad as an ox. But he was oh, so gentle and as sweet as a man could be. Everybody wanted to do duty with me because I had an automobile. Otherwise, the bus was the mode of transportation. Some went on bicycles.

"I loved going with this particular fellow because I was sure I was going to have good experiences. We fastened the little boy's bike to the car and let him have the thrill of riding in the car with us, and we started for the home. He directed us through alleyways and unheard of streets and at last we were there. This time we actually had to crawl through a passageway to the room in back where we found the patient lying on a board-framed bed. We dismissed our little guide and started to examine the mother and found she was ready but not in active labor.

"My Jefe was very tired, so he lay down on a pallet next to her. He looked just right there with his patched pants – clean every day. When he got comfortable, he turned to me and said, 'Miltone, wake me up when you see the head.' And he was asleep. It was a cold winter night, and I was freezing in that room. There was a dirt floor and no heating of any kind. The only place I could sit was on the bed with the Indian woman who was now sitting up. I tried to talk with her in the hope that this would take my mind off my cold limbs. She told me this was to be her 14th child. I asked her, 'Is this the first time you have had a doctor help you to deliver your baby?'

"Her answer was, 'Yes, this is the first time. Before this, my neighbor has come in to help me.'

"I was curious. 'How did you deliver the others?'

"She told me, 'Como los indios,' like the Indians.

"'Tell me what you mean....like the Indians do.'

"She felt like talking, and I was about to learn something I had never even heard of before. She said, 'Here, I will show you. You sit on the bed and put your arms under my arms.' She squatted down so that her knees were on her abdomen. The head of the fetus now was forward to descend through her ample pelvis. After 13 babies, her muscles were so flabby her abdominal muscles could not contract, but this position forced pressure to be borne by her knees and thighs against the abdomen. Very quickly during this demonstration, she reached down under her dress and brought out the baby. Like magic.

"Filled with wonder, I said, 'What are we doing here?' Civilization in this case, only confused the issue. I woke my chief. 'Jefe, jefe, here is the baby!'

The days in Mexico gradually were coming to an end. While his Mexican classmates were preparing to embark on their year of required social service, Milton was applying for internships in the U.S. He wanted to return to Miami or Los Angeles, but many hospitals did not want or could not accept foreign medical school graduates, and the proper school documentation of his completion of studies in Guadalajara was delayed. He and Marcie had written many letters to the Traeger family asserting their desire to live and work in Florida, but as it turned out, he would never return there except for brief visits.

Cedars of Lebanon Hospital in Los Angeles had been the only internship site to accept him of those to which he had applied in California or Florida. He was to begin there July 1, 1955; in mid-June, however, he was still in Guadalajara waiting for his certificate. He and Marcie had sold all of their furniture and had moved into a hotel, ready to head north. The papers didn't materialize; the school wanted him to repeat some exams, but he would not be able to take them until the following year. Milton was in an anxious bind. He drove home to Los Angeles.

An odd turn of events altered his life at this point. As a native English speaker, he had helped several of his classmates apply to schools in the States. They had all urged him to apply wherever they were seeking placements. Usually he refused, as he thought he was already set in Los Angeles, but his good friend Walter was so persistent that Milton agreed to apply to a Hawaiian hospital along with him – Saint Francis in Honolulu – just to get the man off his back. When the position at Cedars fell through, and with a supportive letter in hand from the university president and medical school dean, he immediately wired Honolulu. The next day, Sister Maureen from Saint Francis cabled back,"Come at once." The next morning, he and Marcie were on a plane headed to the Islands. When they stepped off the plane, Walter and the other interns and residents greeted them with orchid leis and Aloha spirit. In Los Angeles, the smog had stimulated several severe asthma attacks. When he deplaned in Honolulu, he cautiously took a deep breath, as he had done in a Florida post office years before, and knew immediately that he had come home.

In the ensuing years, Milton began to fit himself so thoroughly into the Hawaiian way of life that he came to feel as though he had been born there. But he never forgot his expressive second language and would always enjoy speaking Spanish. Nor did his love of Mexico diminish; he returned there whenever possible for medical meetings and vacations.

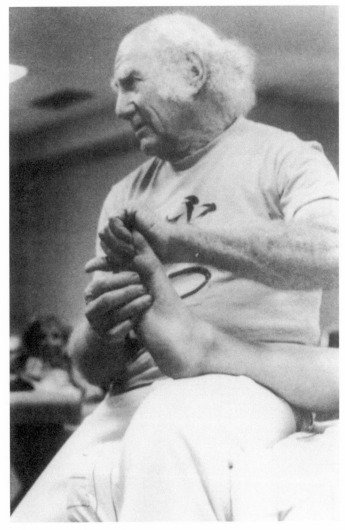

Working the foot, Montreal

6

It's Not The Technique

The practitioners are in Laguna Hills, at the hotel near Milton's home, to refresh their skills and gain some precious personal contact with Milton in his waning days. Siegrit Salkowitz comes as a tutor from Germany, where she has sponsored trainings since 1987, seeding the country with forty certified practitioners in less than six years. Tan and slim, her intense, deep blue eyes silently bespeak strength and a calm wisdom. Four practitioners are here from Canada, four more from Oregon. Others have flown in from Michigan, Florida, Massachusetts, and Texas to join several from California. Two Trager Institute instructors run the class, or try to, never sure what Milton will do or say next, adapting to his desires as best they can.

One of the instructors, Cathy Hammond, is a psychologist and dancer who leads trainings in San Diego and elsewhere around the world. She was an early student of Milton and has written with him the only book describing the movement education aspect of his work – Mentastics – that is, mental gymnastics. Bright and enthusiastic, she inspires and encourages all of her students with her kind words and dancer's energy. Bill Scholl, an instructor from Buda, Texas, looks studious and patiently thoughtful with his beard and glasses. Wearing sweat clothes and running shoes, he observes the practitioners carefully, stepping in with helpful suggestions and word images to remind them of, and focus them on, the feeling of the work.

Although Milton is approaching 85 years and needs his wheeled walker to get to the classroom from the parking lot, he puts it aside when he teaches. He is impatient today, the first day of training. He wastes no energy, not a single movement, and pares his teaching down to the basics: "It is the mind, it is not the body; my job is reaching the mind." As he observes one practitioner after another working on their colleagues, he approaches each one, saying very little, waving them to the side as he demonstrates, then making them cover his hands with theirs as he works, to give them the feeling of it. If he says anything, it is brief and utterly to the point: "Feel it; more indifferent; more positiveness." Where someone has a special problem – a weak shoulder, a painful back, a stiff chest – he lingers, softly exploring the feel of the tissues beneath his gentle hands until he feels the most subtle of changes, the feeling of the mind catching the message and causing the body to alter its very structure.

In the late afternoon, tired from hours of teaching, he slumps onto a table to rest, while around him these advanced students work softly on their partner's bellies. A little earlier, Milton had demonstrated his approach to this vulnerable and intimate area, resting his hand on the exposed abdomen of one of the students for two or three minutes, waiting confidently and quietly, experiencing internally the softness that the belly should have.

Two tables away, a woman whose belly has just been worked begins to sob quietly. Her partner comforts her. Milton senses the situation and comes directly over, talking tenderly but with firmness. "Go;" he says, as he touches her head, "when you cry, really make it count." She begins to sob in great heaves for several minutes; when she stops, she has changed, emerging peaceful and refreshed, her eyes lively, her face rosy.

Milton will work two more days in this manner, demonstrating his work on one part of the body and watching the practitioners practice there, then moving to another area – neck, legs, belly, shoulders, back. Each day he seems to gain strength. The second day he recounts a dream he had had the night before of one of the practitioners, whose body is heavy, her shape distorted. She had dreamed of him that same night, as a teacher of hieroglyphics. He spends extra time with her this second day; she begins to absorb his feeling in silent communication, and he is convinced that great changes will be coming to her soon. They stand together, an intense, almost palpable bond of feeling between them now.

The practitioners, experienced as they are, hang on his every word and watch every nuance of his work as though they were beginning students. While his principles remain unchanged, their meanings sink in more deeply the more developed the practitioner is. A man with a rigid ribcage lies on his belly. Milton repeatedly smoothes his back with his hands, from the pelvis up and out through the shoulder. His long, graceful arms and soft sensitive fingers seem to surround the body in safety. Wearing snug, white pants held up by suspenders over a rose-colored tee shirt with the dancing cloud insignia, his ring of grayish white hair flung out around his head, he looks like a mime artist, communicating everything through movement. He is not massaging, he is impressing on the man's mind the feeling of length, integration, and softness of the entire torso. He lifts the man's left arm as it hangs over the edge of the padded table, weighing it.

"Do this, often," Milton declares, his voice carrying to all of the practitioners in the room.

"Weigh the arm, let it become heavier and heavier each time. I want you always to create more distance between the shoulder and the middle of the back. And when you have that distance, then let your mind create more distance. I'm saying it right. Let your mind make more distance."

When the man rises from the table, Milton shows him the way he wants that arm and shoulder to feel. He slowly waves his own arm out to the side, like a palm frond in the breeze. He describes the motion as indifferent. The man follows the motion with his own arm.

"No, that's just lazy; make it indifferent," Milton tells him, a little sharply, as he repeats the subtle motion. This time the man gets it. "He can be different now because he has experienced something different."

With the training over, and after a day of rest, Milton returns to the classroom, this time to meet with the Trager Institute's twelve Instructors, most of whom were among his earliest students. They are together for a week of meetings, first in Laguna with Milton and then in Mill Valley, north of San Francisco. They exchange reports on their personal work; although they all have their individual styles, they have pledged to keep the work consistent and as close to the source as possible. They struggle to communicate in words this feeling-based and elusive art in order to make the training uniform for students from so many backgrounds, so many countries. How can you certify a practitioner on the basis of feeling? Milton has said so many times, "It's not the technique; it's not a matter of moves." In describing how he knows what to do for difficult problems, he has said,"I suddenly know what to do for them, how really to begin. I wait for this, never force it, wait to feel the patient, his rhythms, his blocks, taking in the communication. The way this happens is not so much from knowledge or intellect as from a source I cannot explain." The instructors wonder how they will communicate this to their students.

Today there is another change in the still evolving teacher. Milton wants them, from now on, to spend more time working on hands in the early training of students. There is much to learn, much to change in the body by feeling the hands and letting them soften and loosen, he says. The instructors are disappointed to learn that he will spend only one day with them. They still need his inspiration and his knowledge to help them carry on and teach his seemingly easy and therefore so difficult art. Silently, many of them have asked themselves what will happen when Milton is no longer able to teach. Although they have taught and worked together for many years, will they have the talent, the power, and the skill to carry on the work? Will they be able to manage it themselves?

Hyman Traeger, Milton's father

Bertha Traeger, Milton's mother

The earliest existing photo of Milton (seated front and center) with Miami postal workers

Traeger family business – left to right: Joe, Nat, Bertha, Sam

AGILITY---Milton Treager, Miami Beach's athletic mail man appears in a special Fox film at the Lincoln theater.

Miami papers notice Milton once he makes the newsreels.

Miami's acrobatic mailman is discovered, Chicago Sunday Tribune, January 10, 1937.

WHY—WHAT HAVE WE HERE?

It's just Milton Traeger, Miami's "whistling postman," delivering a letter on his Beach route in a rather novel fashion—with a back flip. He does it all day and never tires.

More hijinks from Milton

The beach acrobat (right) with "sis" Sarah and Dave

Milton and Marcie, 1945

The Traeger Family – Top: Sister Sarah, Hyman, Bertha; Bottom: Brothers Joe, Sam, Milton, Dave

A flamboyant Milton with his race car, Miami

Milton in his days as a general practice M.D.

Getting back in acrobatic shape, Hawaii, 1961

Milton on the medical school soccer team, (top left)

Milton and Emily in their Hawaii apartment

Milton and the author

7

The Beach Boy Doctor

Milton landed in Hawaii only three days before he was to start work. He launched into the internship year at St. Francis Hospital and began his rotation through the various medical specialty departments. Here again he was the only American; almost all of the other interns, residents, and staff physicians were Asian. As Milton took up residence in the intern cottage and Marcie moved in with the nurses until their apartment was ready, they splurged on a Guadalajara school chum's 1946 Chrysler and brand new television. He liked the work immediately; his asthma was almost gone and he felt himself relaxing for the first time in years. He wrote to his family,"I'm a natural with these people, and make them happy;" the hospital priest had told him how much the staff appreciated his joyful presence. He enjoyed the many races, customs, and dialects he encountered, the casual dress and simplicity of the people. He also loved the simplicity of communication, the use of phrases like, "where hurt?", "I fix," "hurt all gone," and "poor dockta no got hair." He took time to run at the beach, shedding the extra weight he had put on during his student years, and wrote letters home informing his acrobatic brother Sam in detail about the progress he was making in reviving his rusty athletic skills.

In surgery, his first rotation, he scrambled to learn the surgical knots so as not to make a fool of himself. Soon, he wrote, remembering his father's skill, he was,"almost as fast as the Chief, when he was basting a lapel." Also during those three months of surgery, he witnessed an event that impressed him in the same way that his experience in Los Angeles had years before when his rigid Parkinson's disease patient so dramatically loosened his neck while absorbed in watching a tennis match. On this occasion, the surgeons wheeled in a patient so stiff he had to turn his entire body to make any one part move. Yet when the anesthesiologist put him under, the man's body relaxed so completely that he needed several people to turn him over. As soon as he began to regain consciousness, his body stiffened part by part, until he finally returned to his initial rigid state. Milton's earlier conviction was further validated: it was the mind that was responsible for bodily patterns of both relaxation and tension, and important changes in the musculature could be accomplished by altering patterned blocks in the mind.

Marcie returned to art studies, taking classes at the YWCA while Milton worked, and she began learning to play the ukulele. She and Milton gradually joined a beach crowd that regularly danced the hula, played instruments, and sang together. Still a great believer in a diet of fruits and vegetables, she had her juicer sent over from the mainland; she treated Milton with celery and carrot juice for leg pains brought on by long hours of standing in surgery, which caused an old knee injury to flare up. She worried about him eating too much meat and fish at the hospital when he stayed overnight there.

Milton quickly began exploring possible residencies to follow his internship year. He still resolutely intended to return to Florida or Los Angeles, but the same obstacles that prevented a mainland internship resurfaced to block him. Those difficulties and his interest in the mind convinced him finally to remain in Hawaii for a year of residency in psychiatry at the Territorial Hospital in Kaneohe. He intended after that year to return to the States, but when he travelled back to Mexico to make up his exams, he discovered that he would not receive his final paperwork until two years later, at which time he would have to return once more to Mexico for the final professional exams. Even so, he hoped at least to take a year's course in Medicine at the University of Southern California or the University of Miami. These possibilites were never realized, however, and he ultimately spent two years at Kaneohe against the beautiful backdrop of the Koolau Mountains, which he described later.

"In my mind there is no place so beautiful and awe-inspiring as that range. I never minded driving to work because it was a pleasure to go through the pass from Honolulu, over the Pali, to the other side. It was so peaceful and beautiful I truly loved the trip. Whoever planned the hospital felt the location would have a soothing effect on the patients. At that time we had close to 1500 patients with all degrees of mental illness. When local people think somebody is *pupule* (Hawaiian for crazy) they say, 'you belong Kaneohe.'

"I will never forget my first night as duty officer. I had to make the rounds of the acute men's and women's wards, plus the hospital wards, and a few other duties besides such as admitting new patients. This went on until the morning crew came on duty. Physicals had to be done on the new patients. Then they had to be admitted to the proper wards. Medications had to be prescribed. That first time when I went to the women's ward something happened to me that was a first. There were 120 women, many of them quite young. Now, I have never even come close to being a ladies' man – in fact, I didn't have a date until I was 21. I liked women; I guess I was shy. These hospitalized women were falling all over themselves trying to get to me. They suddenly developed mysterious maladies that required instant attention. All wanted to be talked to, and some were exposing parts they wanted examined. They were making all kinds of excuses to have me take them down the hall to my office. Once there they contrived to have me touch them. They stroked my hair, patted my fanny when I walked past them. They made such a fuss over me that I was overcome by the whole thing. I caught myself up and reminded myself that these were mentally disturbed or grossly psychotic females. But I still got a charge out of all this unusual attention. Fortunately, I became conditioned to all this in a very short time. But I never forgot how hungry they were for male attention."

The Saturday night dances that the hospital arranged for the patients gave Milton the opportunity to practice one of his favorite pastimes. It also gave the women patients a fresh opportunity to snuggle close to him; he was tagged every few steps and danced with dozens of them each week. Meanwhile, he had to keep a watchful eye open for other dancers who might be breaking the rules by wandering off into the night together; in fact, he spent considerable time at St. Francis persuading the patients to restrain their sexual impulses toward one another. Deeply compassionate as always, however, he enjoyed their pleasure in the dances and the luaus, which added spice to their routine days. He honed his psychological skills while working with these patients and learned to utilize their way of perceiving the world to help them in practical ways. Those he could not help he accepted with humor and grace. He came to believe that many of these patients had simply regressed to less demanding psychological states when they found themselves unable to withstand the unbearable pressures of their lives. He was endlessly patient, teaching them practical living skills and relieving their daily anxieties.

Milton had an intuitive knack for psychiatry and enjoyed it but also knew instinctively that he could not sit endlessly listening to neurotic complaints for an entire career. His pleasure came from the simple successes that brought relaxation to the faces of disturbed patients and erased their stress lines. He was as easy with these severely disturbed patients as he had been with an ordinary patient complaining of back pain. He took an interest in them as people, and he liked them. Although he eventually dropped his plan of becoming a psychiatrist, he saw clearly that the skills he was developing in Kaneohe would serve him well in general practice, where so many physical problems have psychological underpinnings.

As the end of his second year of residency approached, Milton was still having problems with his licensure. He was unable to sit for the Florida Board licensing exam on a paper technicality, and he failed the Hawaii territorial Board exam as well. He was tired, depressed, and frustrated and felt that he had let his family down. Ultimately, he abandoned the idea of practicing on the mainland and decided to stay on in Hawaii, which was feeling more and more like home every day.

Milton faced a hard decision at that point: to work for Kaiser, a large health maintenance organization, or open his own practice. After years of earning little money, an assured salary looked appealing compared to the risks involved in starting a new office. Here again, though, an oddity – this time a material one – meshed with his own idiosyncrasies and jogged him into a decision that would determine his future direction. On this occasion, he was visiting a friend at the Waikiki Medical Office, just across from the Royal Hawaiian Hotel, who was encouraging him to opt for Kaiser.

"While we were talking, I noticed the room we were in. It was an odd shaped room, but one that would be perfect for the strange looking desk that I had bought and stored away in Los Angeles. It was three-cornered like a George Washington hat. The thought flashed through my mind that it would look great in that office. Since this doctor was going to work at Kaiser, the office became available, and I believe that is how I happened to open an office in Waikiki. I realized I had to be free to do my own thing. I could not work for someone else, as regimentation was not for me."

Milton's irregular academic history was still haunting him.The Hawaii Medical Board was reluctant to issue a license to someone from a foreign medical school who had never attended a regular college in the United States. Finally, his friends and colleagues rallied to his side; support for him was so strong that ultimately the state legislature passed a bill with his name on it, authorizing the medical board to issue his license.

For the next twenty years, Milton would be "the Waikiki Doctor," serving the needs of its oddly varied population, starting at $7 a visit. After one month of practice, he was already seeing a few people for his special treatments, others for psychotherapy, and still more for general medicine and walk-in care. After three years as a poorly paid intern and resident and six years as a student, the prospects looked good. He wrote to his family, "This is such an easy buck, that I have to smile when I collect it. If I really get busy, I could net before taxes $16,000-$18,000 per year, which is all the money any sensible person should need." He and Marcie had moved into an apartment three blocks from the office and were having fun and making a little extra money buying and selling the quickly appreciating apartments in their building.

Milton's practice quickly grew and flourished. He was as comfortable treating native Hawaiians and speaking pidgin English with them as he was catering to tourists distraught over falling ill while on vacation. Nothing pleased him more than being accepted by the local Hawaiians, and dancing the hula during his free moments was one of the ways he garnered their love and respect.

"We had a ball, and soon I was joining the beach gang, who love to see a *haole* really do a good hula. Whenever old Dave saw me coming down to swim, he picked up his Uke and announced, 'Da Dockta is going to dance.' Or he just started to play my favorite piece, and I had to dance for him. We had a great feeling for each other, and I appreciated his acceptance of me. All I needed was to see Dave's face light up in approval of the dance. This went on for all the years that I was in Waikiki.

"One morning I came in to my office. From the door arrangement, I knew my nurse had a patient waiting for me in the treatment room. I went in, and there was a woman sitting on the table with a thermometer in her mouth. I sat down on the stool opposite her to wait until it was time to read the thermometer. But she grabbed the instrument out of her mouth and nearly screamed at me, 'What are you doing here?' You can imagine my surprise, but I answered quietly, 'I'm the doctor—this is my office.' This was too much for her. 'You're the doctor? You're the beach boy I saw dancing in front of the Reef Hotel today!'"

As a general practitioner, Milton treated the whole array of medical problems that the family doctor encounters. But he was always aware of the psychological currents beneath many physical complaints, and he never tired of teaching and counseling his patients. He was ceaselessly amazed and amused at the ignorance of people in relation to their own bodies.

In his otherwise standard medical practice, Milton continued his hands-on therapeutic work. He usually set aside the first hour in the office to see one patient each day who needed his special therapy.

Over the course of those years, he continued to develop his feeling and understanding of the body; slowly he began to formulate and find words for the principles underlying his work. He was discovering an ever wider range of problems that responded to his hands-on approach. During these years, thousands of people with chronic back pain and many other ailments walked out of his office, after one of his sessions, free of pain and happy, if not quite clear about what had just happened. When he returned to California on yearly vacations, there were always people waiting for his unique touch; some of his previous patients from earlier days in Los Angeles even travelled to Hawaii to receive help that no one else at home could duplicate.

Back in California, Milton had periodically worked on Marcie's friend Emily, and he did so again when she visited in Hawaii. A successful businesswoman on the mainland, she was in the process of buying apartments for herself and her mother in Honolulu in the same building as Milton and Marcie's, and this proximity helped to revive their friendship, as did their mutual interest in Transcendental Meditation, a method named and promoted by the Maharishi Mahesh Yogi of India.

Milton and Marcie had already begun daily practice in this form of meditation. Marcie, who had practiced yoga for many years and was fascinated by eastern spirituality, had been excited in 1958 when she learned that the Maharishi was in Hawaii. She met him at a health fair booth in Honolulu and in her direct way invited him to a vegetarian lunch in their apartment. Milton was not particularly interested in the Maharishi; yet, on the day of the lunch, he felt compelled to leave Saint Francis Hospital, where he was interning, and go home at midday. "Ah, at last I am meeting the good doctor!" the Maharishi said in greeting. They sat for hours intently discussing Milton's special therapy; when he asserted that it worked by reaching the unconscious mind, the Maharishi corrected him. "You don't realize you are working in the Superconscious." He initiated the couple in his method of meditation; they were among the first eight initiates in the western hemisphere. The Maharishi was planning to leave Hawaii and wanted Milton to carry on the work for him there, but Milton refused.

This early encounter would prove significant in the years to come, as Transendental Meditation gained hundreds of thousands of adherents in the United States and elsewhere and ultimately led to important research and subsequent changes in thinking in the American medical community. Those changes, after many years, would ultimately help to open doors for Milton's work.

Emily became even more deeply involved in Transcendental Meditation than the Tragers. She had also been initiated in Hawaii, by the man who the Maharishi had left in charge of carrying on his work, and she later travelled to California to meet the master himself. She wanted him to personally initiate her; he told her to return the next day with flowers, a handkerchief, and fruit. As they sat on the floor together, he asked her to tell him her mantra, the word or phrase she used in meditation. During her initiation she had been told not to reveal the mantra, and she refused his request. At this he threw his head back and roared with laughter. "I have found myself a confidential secretary; she won't even tell me her mantra!" For the next several months, she was with him constantly, helping him spread his work in California and beyond.

Milton's idyllic life in Hawaii was shattered when Marcie grew seriously ill with cancer. She rejected all medical treatment in favor of her natural dietary cures. Milton watched helplessly as she quickly deteriorated and died in 1962. He was devastated, having depended on his wife's strength, support, and companionship for 23 years. He called on the Levine family in California for help in his need, but it was Emily, who was in town at the time to take ownership of and furnish her apartment, who stayed and helped him the most during his grief. He spent long hours after work visiting with her and her mother and having meals in their apartment. She helped take his mind off his loss by finding small tasks for him in redecorating his apartment, which had originally been furnished with Marcie in mind. Their relationship deepened over the next three years, but Emily grew concerned that she wasn't helping him and that he needed to move ahead with his life. She decided to go on a world cruise, and when Milton came to dinner one night, she showed him the tickets and itinerary. He sat quietly listening, then asked Emily's mother if he could have a few minutes alone with her. Milton turned to Emily at that point and suddenly proposed marriage, to her surprise.

They were married at City Hall in 1965. Along with the usual vows, he pledged never to make her hurry, and she promised never to serve him eggplant or squash. Once they married, his attachment to her grew to be as complete and necessary for his happiness as his union with Marcie had been. Gradually, with her help, he picked up the pieces of his life and went on.

Their condo was right on the beach, a stone's throw from the office. Milton would routinely walk to work, greeting the people whom he had come to know so well over the years. Tourists back for return vacations would recognize and want to talk with the gentle, understanding doctor they had consulted on a previous visit. Milton felt like a country doctor. He would walk back home at noon, eat, and nap as he had learned to do in his Mexico days, then return to the office at 2:00 PM for an afternoon of seeing patients.

As a vacation capital for Americans and Asians, a rest and recuperation stopover for servicemen from Vietnam, and a haven for hippies and other free spirits, Hawaii had more than its share of problems with sexually transmitted disease. Milton treated the venereal diseases and counselled his patients on their concerns about the implications of these diseases for their relationships and their sexual partners. In the Navy, he had helped treat hundreds of men for the same problem, and he was concerned professionally about its epidemic spread. The Hawaiian Medical Association asked him to head the Venereal Disease section of its Communicable Disease Committee; he appeared on television shows and frequently spoke at schools on the subject.

While Milton was genuinely concerned about this work and his general medical practice, his gratification as a doctor clearly came from observing the bewildering and at times hilarious variety of human behavior, and finding ways to create feeling relationships with his patients. Over the years, he grew proficient in handling the many complaints, from serious to ridiculous, that his varied practice brought him. Always the teacher, he patiently filled in the often large gaps in his patients' knowledge of anatomy, hygiene, and common sense. His medical treatments were conventional, apart from his special body movement work, his advice always practical and down to earth. But his affection for his patients was unusual, and he felt it even for the most recalcitrant, self-destructive, and ignorant of them. Returning from the office at lunch or dinner, Milton amused Emily with the funny and curious daily happenings in the office. He began to jot down anecdotes from the practice, dropping them in an old cigar box that Emily kept for that purpose. One year they enrolled in a writing class and pieced those scraps together into an almost book-length manuscript.

Emily described at some length the pleasurable routine of their life in Hawaii, and one of Milton's treatments, in a letter to Turnley Walker, the author and screenwriter whom Milton had treated for post-polio paralysis back in the early 1940's. At the time of the correspondence, in 1975, he was gathering material from her for a book he had begun to write about Milton's life. By then, Milton and Emily had coined a term for the movements that he practiced and taught others. What he had previously called Rhythmic Harmonization was now Mentastics, meaning mental gymnastics. By then, too, Milton had become a "hotel doctor." While other doctors practiced pediatrics or gynecology, he had become a "Tourist Specialist." He made the rounds of the Waikiki hotels and was called whenever any of the guests needed a doctor.

"When he awakens in the morning, he is alert to the day, never groggy or unwilling to get up. Like an acrobat, he draws his knees up and makes himself into a ball and rolls out of bed. He flips his legs right and left as he goes toward the bathroom. In a couple minutes he is back with the question, 'Shall I shave first, or do we meditate?'

"We go into the living room, where Milton sits in a chair and I sit on the sofa. We face the East. It is about 6:30-7:00 AM. We sit for about 20-30 minutes and come out in a lovely state of peace. We agree that it is a beautiful way to start the day. He joins me on the sofa, and I go into his arms and he holds me. The meditation still has us in its spell and we are quiet for a few minutes. Often he says, 'No matter what happens today, it cannot be as wonderful as what we have right now.'

"We get on our feet and Milton starts his Mentastics, and I do my best to follow his professional method of awakening the body. With a gesture or a word, he has me performing like a dancer, feeling beautiful all over. When I stop to think that he had to teach me coordination between my hands and feet when I first came to him for help years ago, I am filled with wonder that this is me moving around the room joyously. He tells me that no one has to go through the years of training that he followed to get where he is, but that, by his projection to me, I can achieve this perfection by feeling what he is showing me. I have to accept this, for here I am moving about with complete body freedom. I am not discouraged when he tells me that we have both only scratched the surface of our potential. He never sets goals for himself.

"From our *lanai* where we have a garden with vegetables and fruit, if we turn to the right, we look at the mountains. Then we go through the living room to our kitchen where we look out at Diamond Head. Here Milton stands at the sink and eats his breakfast of papaya, an orange, and a couple bananas. It never varies. All the while, he is looking out at the ever-changing sights of the ocean and the mountain. Surfers and swimmers are fourteen floors below. Sometimes he turns on the radio and dances to some special music he likes. I am always delighted with his wonderful interpretation of the music. All of a sudden he says that he guesses he should consider going to the office. He is never late for anything. He will not wear a watch, or any other piece of jewelry. He says things get in his way. He must be free. I finally succeeded in convincing him that he should wear whites to the office. We had special short-sleeved jacket-shirts and unbelted slacks made to order of washable polyester. 'I'll be damned if I'm going to have you pressing my clothes.' And that settled it.

"His shoes and socks are always in the same place beside the door, and, as he gets ready to put them on, he alerts me that he is nearly ready to leave. He puts his arms out and we fold up in an embrace that is suited for a couple about to part for one to go across the world for a long stay. We embrace without a word.

"As he walks to his office by way of the Reef Hotel, he greets the bellboys and the clerks, waves at the manager, exchanges remarks with the taxi drivers, and gives free advice to all. 'Hey, doc, I'm coming to the office today.' 'What do you want to come to the office for. Talk to me now – save a buck.' They are delighted with this special attention from the doctor. When the manager needs a flu shot and is too busy to get to the office, Milt brings the shot with him when he comes home for lunch.

"After he gets out of the Reef Hotel, he walks along Kalia Road to Lewers, then left on Lewers to Kalakaua, after passing the hotels he serves along the way. One block on Kalakaua to Royal Hawaiian Avenue, left turn into the entrance of the Waikiki Medical Building. He doesn't bother with the elevator. In the same rhythm he has enjoyed the whole way, he now goes up the stairs to the second floor and through the swinging doors to the waiting room to his office in the corner.

"Behind the reception desk sits his nurse, Michiko (Gladys) Yamamoto. She has been with him since 1960. She does everything that has to be done in that office except be a doctor. When she thinks he is not charging enough, she lets him know. He hates to collect money; he just wants to do his job and is happy he has somebody to take care of the rest.

"He does a Table Treatment at 8:30 nearly every morning. The room in which it takes place is just large enough to get the job done. In California, before he became an M.D., he would stand at his table 8 to 10 hours a day. His hands and arms would become so sore he would have to soak them between treatments. In the center of his treatment room is a blue vinyl, covered table that takes up most of the room. This is the fourth table that he has built; this one should last a lifetime. It stands on 4 x 4 legs, 2 x 6 sides, and 2 x 6 boards for the top. The top has a five inch thick rubber foam cover, which is tapered around the sides to protect the patients' arms when they hang over. The patient must be completely comfortable. The vinyl cover is stretched tightly all around—measures six feet plus by two feet. There is one straight-backed chair to hold the patient's clothes. Milton has just enough room left so that he can move around the table.

"Michiko gets the patient ready with a simple gown and a sheet on the table. As she comes out of the room, she signals Milton that all is ready. She knows that he will be unavailable for the next hour. She understands the importance to him and to his patient of this time, for she has seen the outcomes of these treatments over the years.

"This morning's treatment was a thirty-four-year old Tahitian woman. She was a chunky 140 pounder, suffering from chronic low back pain of three years' duration. She had been treated by several doctors. She doesn't speak or understand English, but fortunately her husband does and acts as interpreter from his chair in the corner. She was full of hostility and had a look of doubt that anything good could come out of this situation she was in. She had the look of 'I am here only because my husband insisted on it.' Milton went about his business in spite of her attitude. He has never told a patient that he must cooperate or relax so he could help them. That is his job to accomplish.

"He started as he usually does, with the patient on her back. He took her by the shoulders and pushed her down about a foot, so that he could straddle the table, which he claims is a very comfortable position for him. Before he starts working, he pauses for a moment as if waiting for a signal to tell him he is ready. His hands begin to work in a rhythmic pattern that assures the patient that here is a man who knows what he is doing. A pleasant feeling of confidence that something right is happening comes into the patient, and a certain response comes through to Milton, and both of them know they are on the same wavelength.

"The husband asks why Milton is working on her neck when her pain is in her lower back. Milton answers, 'I'll be at least thirty minutes before I get down there. First, I have to get everything else out of the way and in harmony. By the time I get to her lower back, most of my work will be over, and the back area will be easy.' All through the treatment, Milton has been talking and the husband has been interpreting for his wife. A bonus has come into the room; the man had complained to Milton two days before that he can't relax. He takes medicine for sleep, tranquilizers during the day. The man's voice was changing so that Milton looked over at him. There was a definite change in the man. He was relaxed. He had picked up the feeling that was coming into his wife on the table. By this time, she was completely changed. From the formidable person who had entered the room earlier, she had become pleasant and like a close friend, and all three were in a lovely, peaceful state.

"Milton follows a typical sequence in his work. When he feels he has finished with one part, he goes on to the other. From the neck he goes to the feet and legs, then to the chest and belly. The patient turns over on the stomach. Again, Milton works on the feet and legs from that position, to give the feeling of openness and freedom. Next he goes to the right shoulder to break up the set pattern of stiffness and tightness of the area. He then goes down the back slowly, with a rocking, moving motion that is directed by his mind. He is unconsciously searching out painful and blocked areas. When he is satisfied that he has accomplished his goals for that area, he repeats the entire procedure on the left side. This side responds quickly because it has picked up the feeling and pattern of the other side. The brain has actually done the job. Also, while the patient is on the table, Milton gives her the feeling of elongation without effort on her part. He imparts this with his hands by separating her upper back from the lower. From this feeling she will know what her proper posture will be when she is on her feet. She will no longer be compressing the nerves in the lower back, which had been giving her much pain and spasm in the muscles. This new pattern has been implanted in her subconscious mind and it cannot be erased.

"When she is on her feet and dressed, Milton walks with her up and down the long corridor of the building, teaching her how to move her legs freely in proper posture without strain. This is quickly picked up in a natural manner, and the patient is completely free of pain. She is also aware that she now has a chance to function in a normal fashion. What had been a chance meeting of her husband with this tourist doctor has led to a change in two people's lives. He feels, as they do, the wrenching feeling that comes with parting with old and dear friends. And then he has to break away, most reluctantly, to take care of a room full of people who have been waiting for the doctor to look down their throats, tell them to say 'ah; take two of these; no, I don't think you should take the Pearl Harbor cruise today; no, you should not drink while taking this medicine; stay out of the sun for a couple of days.'

"Milton would prefer not to do more than the one treatment a day, but today he cannot refuse to see the friend of one of his long-time patients. The latter had been cured of migraines by Milton, and her friend has the same problem. He starts to work on her neck, as he usually does, and finds much there. But, in a very short time, the muscles relaxed and the headache vanished. This was almost impossible for her to believe. He then told her that he believed that, with this quick response, it was very probable that she would soon be rid of the attacks. Milton is very conservative about making promises of cures, but he has been working with a number of migraine cases lately and has reason to be encouraged by the response."

Milton and Emily enjoyed this active and relatively carefree existence for ten years. They still had the real estate bug, buying and selling apartments in their building as the prices kept steadily rising. That ended when they almost lost their shirts in an attractive, but ill-advised, business investment with a friend. The legal and financial ramifications of that venture distressed them for several years. Milton played golf on Wednesdays; they socialized minimally with a small circle of friends and occasionally went to the theater. The rest was work. By the mid 1970's, the pace was beginning to wear Milton down. As the hotel doctor, he was on call until 10:00 PM every night. Often he came home too tired to do more than eat dinner and sleep. He fantasized about retiring to write, perhaps dabble in acupuncture, and do one of his treatments a day.

At a deeper level, Milton was also frustrated. He had gone to medical school to secure the credentials needed to teach his special technique to doctors and have it accepted by them, yet aside from a few of his colleagues who knew of his work, he had never found an audience for his knowledge. When he first arrived in Hawaii twenty years earlier, he had offered his services in rehabilitation to the staff of Shriner's Hospital for Crippled Children. They had refused to let him touch a single child. He was hurt and angry at that rejection.

Even after earning his license, he discovered that other doctors either lacked interest in his hands-on work or openly scoffed at it. It seemed that his ideas simply did not fit into their notions of how the body functioned or how medicine should be properly practiced. And he had trouble explaining the work in standard medical jargon. He did not like being treated like a crackpot. He had never wanted to promote himself as an individual and had never developed the skills needed to promote his work; ultimately, he grew discouraged and began to doubt that he could ever effectively convey his highly developed but essentially nonverbal knowledge. Yet the desire still stirred strongly in him; this was what he knew and did best.

Once again, a seemingly chance occurrence was to significantly change the course of his life, at age 65. At a dinner party in 1973, he struck up a conversation with a well-known psychologist named Corsini and tried for the hundredth time to explain his work and its effects. Dr. Corsini could not comprehend it. Milton invited him to go to a quiet room and experience the work. Emily wrote about the effect of that encounter on the psychologist.

"He came out of the room a bewildered man. His own theories and teachings were somehow shaken. He wanted to know why

Milton wasn't known in the proper places. Well...several months later Milton got a letter from Esalen telling him that Dr. Corsini had been there and had told them about Milton and his work. Would he be interested in demonstrating the work there?"

Milton agreed to go, but he wondered if it would lead to still more disappointment. It seemed that no matter how effective he was in his individual treatments, he could not effectively explain them. His desire and his disappointment were triggered yet again when he returned to Mexico in November of 1974, just before his scheduled appearance at Esalen, to attend an international general practice conference. Through his old medical school classmates, he received invitations to demonstrate his work at two hospitals in Mexico City. In the first, he treated a man suffering from stress-related chronic gastrointestinal problems. With one touch, Milton could feel the rigidity throughout his body that the other physicians had missed entirely. After the treatment, the man grasped his hand in gratitude for the relief he felt. The doctors seemed impressed, but they had no idea what had really happened or how it had been accomplished.

He was asked in the second hospital to treat a woman who had had multiple surgeries for back ailments. She had to be assisted to the table, obviously in pain. She had been so traumatized by her previous treatments that when Milton reached out a gentle hand to touch her neck, she recoiled in terror. With his customary soothing patience, Milton began to work with her. She changed visibly under his hands; by the time he had finished, she rolled easily off the table, free of pain. She was so grateful she insisted on escorting Milton and Emily around town for the next two days, pledging her lifelong friendship. But the observing doctors concluded that he had performed hypnosis on her. They had no other way medically of explaining to themselves what they had witnessed.

Nonetheless, Milton and Emily were excited at possibilities on the horizon. He had been asked in Hawaii to see a seven-year-old girl with cerebral palsy who could not walk and was greatly distressed at falling behind her schoolmates. After one session, she had progressed so rapidly that her regular physical therapist insisted on attending the next treatment. Milton soon had the girl walking up and down stairs; the therapist was so astounded and impressed that she arranged for a demonstration at the same Shriner's Hospital where he had not been allowed to put a finger on a child twenty years earlier. This time they received him warmly and admired his work. Milton had also been invited to demonstrate his work at the University of California at Los Angeles, in the laboratory of Thelma Moss, who was using Kirlian photography to measure energetic changes in practitioners who employed their hands for healing purposes. It seemed that recognition was finally coming for his work.

Turnley Walker was also now regularly sending newly written chapters of his book about Milton and his work. Milton felt embarrassed by the glowing and heroic descriptions of his life and his genius; at the same time, he and Emily realized that a published book would probably bring the acceptance that he had wanted for so long. The possibilities were exciting. They anticipated television and radio appearances, opportunities to teach, an audience for the work at last. Somewhere there had to be students to teach. Milton did not know who they might be, but he felt confident that he would recognize them when he saw them. And then there was this intriguing invitation to Esalen.

It was not until June of 1975 that Milton was finally able to set up and keep a teaching date at Esalen Institute. They had never heard of the place and so began to inquire and read about it. What they learned only increased their interest and excitement. Esalen was a meeting and workshop center whose mission was to explore and promote human values and human potential. Set along the rugged and beautiful Big Sur coast of northern California, it was a mecca for explorers of new ideas and alternatives to standard thinking in the humanities and sciences. Many of the ideas and methods that later became identified with the human potential movement and New Age thinking began or gained followers there. That sounded promising.

And so it was that an aging and unusual doctor with an unusual talent, unattached to any movement, New Age or conventional, came face to face with the California counterculture. Somehow it seemed to Milton to be the next move he needed to make.

Entertaining the "beach boys" and other friends in Hawaii

Emily helps the Maharishi Mahesh Yogi establish his presence in the West, 1960

8

The New Age Meets A Master

For Milton Trager, whose hands know everything
that is in this book
GREGORY BATESON
handwritten inscription in a
copy of *Balinese Character*

Milton had originally been scheduled to demonstrate his work at
Esalen in November of 1974. He and Emily flew to Los Angeles for
that purpose in the Fall but ultimately canceled his appearance. In
L.A., Harold Rose, a relation and friend from his first marriage, had
a favor to ask. Would Milton help a severely disabled friend of his?
He could never refuse such a request, as Harold knew. And that
request, in an odd way, proved important as Milton prepared to begin
teaching his work; it showed him a way to accomplish what was to
come at Esalen and beyond.

Reeve Darling, while still in college, had been stricken with progressive muscular dystrophy. Remarkably, though confined to a
wheelchair now and unable to move more than the muscles of his
face, he ran a highly successful management consulting firm with
the help of round-the-clock attendants, drawing strength from his
naturally great spirit and sheer force of will.

Milton went to his home, accompanied by Emily and Harold and
his wife, and listened to the man's story. As a teenager, he had had
bouts of unexpected and unexplained clumsiness, which at the time
he refused to worry about. By age twenty-one, he was on canes.
Then came the wheelchair. He was able to drive a car for another ten
years but finally lost the use of his arms. For a while after that, he
could still feed himself until finally all movement was gone. What
remained were lively eyes, a voice, and a mind, still alert, sensitive,
and intelligent. The rest of him lay inert, covered by a blanket, moved
about and tended by others. Even his head had to be positioned by

an attendant to enable him to look at today's unusual visitor. Although he had never worked on such a problem, Milton simply waded in, without fear or anxiety. He had no plan; he would just play around with a hand to begin with. He later described his thoughts and feelings about the work with Reeve.

"...progressive muscular dystrophy. Can it be halted, somehow turned back, turned around? It seems that this has never happened, and yet....it's funny but I knew before I came here that I would be doing what I'm doing now. It's like we're all alone here, and I have a feeling of complete positiveness about this man and his condition, and before the evening is over something new or different is going to happen. I reached under the blanket for his hand and found it. His hand that had not moved for so long, that had no impulses toward movement left in it. I let my hand feel the weight of his hand, simply feel it. I knew I was confronted with something I had never had to deal with before.

Soon a rhythm was starting, with me holding his right hand, my left hand at his elbow. I kept moving. Moving. In about fifteen minutes I thought I felt him come into the act. Soon after this I was sure I felt him. I looked at him and he looked at me."

At that moment, Reeve felt a part of himself he had not felt for many years. Always open to the potential for change, Milton told him that this was only the beginning. How far it would go no one could know. They arranged for another session the following day in Reeve's office, a plush suite in one of the gleaming new towers of Century City, next to Beverly Hills.

All Reeve wanted was enough movement of his hands to operate the electronic devices that Harold, an expert in biomedical engineering, planned to assemble for him. "Why not?"said Milton. To Reeve's protest that no one had been able to halt muscular dystrophy, much less reverse it, Milton merely shrugged his shoulders. With the help of David Thompson, one of Reeve's assistants, Milton began the second of several sessions, using a padded table set up in the conference room of the suite.

"David and I hoisted Reeve onto the table. He was helpless, dead weight, his neck could not control his head without careful support. He had no self-consciousness whatever at our handling of him, even though Emily was there. David and I stripped him down to his jockey shorts, again no self-consciousness, no affectations, very unusual. Reeve is a remarkable man. Rare man.

"David is strong and sure, tunes in intuitively on what is expected of him, sensitive, quick to learn. Should be grateful to have him as my first student, help me see how it goes.

"Had some idea what to expect after Reeve gave me highlights of his medical story, but still was shocked at the body which that blanket covered at home and the well-tailored business clothes cover here at the office. A big and strong man in his prime, over 200 pounds, I'd say, more than six-feet tall, the shoulder width and heavy bone structure are still there, but the musculature is gone. And he is at least thirty pounds heavier than he should be now, belly sagged and bulged out.

"It was surprising to me that his breathing was so full and even. Partly, I was sure, a matter of exceptional will power and self-training...This was the most seriously damaged person I had ever worked with. The progressive condition would somehow have to be arrested, turned back, before the muscles of breathing were affected. I would have to begin by getting some movement, however slight, back into his hands and arms. His hands. One hand.

"His neck was nearly rigid. He said he had a tightness in his throat. 'Only my voice and eyes move these days,' he had told me. The eyes are clear and quick and very intelligent, expressing a wide and deep range of thought and emotion. He is wide and deep inside that head of his, running this business without strain apparently, no complaints, facing everything.

"I began by relaxing his neck. I guess I was talking quietly to his neck and throat and shoulders, the way I always seem to do. Before long he was murmuring back, something about my being, 'the man who talks to muscles.' The first time I had heard this...

"David was watching me closely and I guess listening to me, too. I liked his eyes. I liked the way he stood, easy and balanced and with a complete naturalness, and the way his hands, lean, strong hands, hung from his wrists, easy and relaxed and ready. I suppose I was trying to figure out what to do with him, how to teach him.

"I worked with Reeve's hand, then the other hand and arm, taking it completely easy, not pressing in the slightest way, feeling expectant and good about what was going to happen, it didn't matter when. It was so easy to be aware of the deep feeling and quiet intensity of the way Reeve was reaching out for connection with me. And beginning to make that connection.

"I brought David closer and for a while just let him sort of feel how my whole body was when I was working. Then I showed him how to pick up Reeve's hand and work with it and with Reeve, just the beginning of this. I tried to work my hands with his, then I had him put his hands over my hands as I did the working. That was good. I could feel the way he was getting it. There was a good, close feeling between us. Again, I let David take the hand and told Reeve to tell David what he must do to make the hand feel like it felt when I was working it.

"Reeve would say, 'Your left hand is too high...too much strength in the other hand...' Things like that. Then I would step in and have David put his hands over mine. Or I would take David's hands and give him the feeling of what it should be. Reeve never lost his connection. 'Yes...that's more like it, that's it...' he would say.

"After two and a half hours, we had all had it. I would see him again the next morning. Emily told me that this would be Thanksgiving morning. I could tell that she felt as I did, that working with Reeve Darling would be a good way to spend part of our Thanksgiving...

"The next morning it began coming. We really got into the swing of it, and Reeve and I were able to bring actual motion and the tiniest touches of strength into both hands. He could even turn his hand in and out and could bring his arms up and down very slightly. Reeve and I were together.

"David was watching, swaying slightly with me, with the way I was moving. I worked with him some, the way I had the day before, teaching him. Emily knew what has happening; she always did. I asked her to come and take Reeve's hand and feel what I was feeling. Her eyes and face began to shine, as if she were in on something that really might be a rebirth...

"I am not sure of what is happening with Reeve or how far it will go. To go only a little way would be remarkable. I have promised him that what happens, what he feels, he will never lose, because it will be there in his mind...

"He has to sleep on his back, has had to do that for so many years...Can anyone know how much will and control that takes: Never turning, never curling up, or stretching. The discomfort, the frustration, the occasional agony that have to be controlled. After much difficulty and pure muscle strength, David and I were able to get Reeve over face down on this temporary treatment table. I got my hands on his back. Before long I felt it responding. We then laboriously got him to a sitting position. He could feel the change that had come into his back and was able to raise his shoulders by himself and wriggle around on his bottom. What a look in his eyes. I could imagine, no, feel his relief. I told him again that what he feels now he can't lose."

It was time for Milton to return to his medical practice. He had passed up his date in Esalen in order to give Reeve his help. In the process, however, he had taught some aspects of his work for the first time. And through this challenge, his own work had developed further.

That was something he would never be able to teach to others, the way in which his own mind developed in close connection with the changes he produced in the minds of his patients. He would work with Reeve again on future trips to Los Angeles, resuming the feeling connection that meant so much to both of them.

The appointment at Esalen was rescheduled for June of the following year. One of the Institute's co-founders, Richard Price, had been a student of Alan Watts, the famed teacher and interpreter of Eastern religious thought. It was Watts who had presented the first seminar there; afterwards, a tradition of informal seminars in that beautiful and rugged coastline watered by natural hot sulphur springs led to the founding of the Institute. Esalen sponsored workshops on matters of fundamental importance, without the academic formality of a typical college. Teachers and students considered basic questions of human relationships, the self, and their place in the cosmos. Religion, philosophy, psychotherapy, and physical development were all part of the eclectic curriculum, and its style and methods were later studied and copied throughout North America and Europe by government agencies, corporations, even universities and churches.

Coming from their circumscribed world of work in Hawaii, a few friends, and relatives in Los Angeles, Milton and Emily were thunderstruck by what they found at Esalen. They loved the feeling of community there. Students and teachers alike were completely informal, strolling and playing along the wide expanses of lawn and the well-tended vegetable gardens that provided much of the food for the communal dining room, and relaxing in the open air baths that overlooked the cool, green ocean waves below.

Stanislav Grof, the psychiatrist, had just finished directing a two-hundred-hour program exploring the relationship between human culture and consciousness. He would later receive a session from Milton, as would Gregory Bateson, the noted anthropologist who was living there at the time. While they waited for their scheduled Wednesday night demonstration, Milton and Emily wandered about, standing out in their Waikiki resort clothes. He ran and danced and moved as he had back on the beaches of Miami years before, while Emily explored and pitched in with the volunteers who tended the gardens. She also scheduled treatment sessions for staff and students who had learned of his presence and wanted to experience his work.

With time on their hands, they asked Dick Price if they could sit in on a class. With his permission, they wandered into a classroom and asked the instructor if they might watch. Milton was enchanted to see that there were no chairs. Everyone reclined on big pillows spread on the floor. The instructor, Betty Fuller, was a frequent seminar leader at Esalen and had been a Resident Fellow there a few years earlier. A former professional actress and a student of Moshe Feldenkrais and Fritz Perls, the Gestalt therapist, she taught Feldenkrais's Awareness Through Movement classes and gave workshops exploring the relationship between motion and emotion.

As she led her students through a series of movements, she was silently suffering with extreme neck pain from an accident sustained some time before. Milton, by virtue of years of sharp observation, saw immediately that she had a problem. After the class, he approached. "How do you do. I'm Dr. Trager; I'd like to help you with your neck." Having been hurt by several well-meaning helpers in the past, and always direct, she replied, "Nobody touches my neck!" Milton, in his gentle way, responded, "I know someone has frightened you or hurt you in the past. My work is very gentle; I won't hurt you. Come, lay down."

Rudeness hadn't worked; she saw no way of getting out of it, so she did as she was told. Soon her head was moving back and forth until she didn't know what was happening or where she was. When she got up, the pain was gone and she was hooked. She had been made to feel that way by only two other people in her life: her mother and Moshe. "How can I learn to do that?" she asked.

Betty and seventy others came to Milton's demonstration the next night. Wednesday nights at Esalen were devoted to informal gatherings where new ideas and methods were presented to anyone who wished to attend. He had selected a model for the demonstration, and when the man came up, Milton, having noticed that many people went to the baths and got massages naked, abruptly asked him, "Do you have your underwear?" "Yep, right here," the man replied. Milton then watched in shocked silence as the man pulled some underwear out of his pocket, dropped his pants, and put them on in front of everyone.

No one in the audience, including many who were well versed in massage and other body therapies, had ever seen anything like what they saw that night. Who was this man, this doctor in a short-sleeved, polyester shirt, sitting astride a table as he worked, joking with the audience and effortlessly tossing the man's neck around with a bizarre combination of supreme self-confidence and supreme surrender? And what did he mean when he said,"It wasn't me. I don't have anything to do with the treatment. I am just scratching the surface."? What was this short, muscular, tan stranger doing when he closed his eyes, a sweet smile on his lips, and disappeared in an internal absorption? What was this hook-up thing? It didn't fit in their New Age vocabulary. Meanwhile, on the table, the man's body moved as though it had no skeleton, like a jellyfish, and when he arose from the table, he was completely at peace, calm, fluid, and refreshed. Milton, the old showman, continued talking and joking, enjoying himself thoroughly.

For the next few days, people clamored to have him work on them. Emily scheduled sessions for him, accommodating everyone she could while ensuring that he didn't overwork himself. Left on his own, he would never refuse anyone; besides, he was basking in his new celebrity. Betty never left their side. She drove them wherever they wanted to go and made a deal with them: in exchange for taking them into San Francisco to shop, they would visit her studio there. They came the next day, and Milton offered to work on her partner Dub Leigh. He told Betty to stand next to him as he worked on Dub's neck then directed her to "cover my hands." He continued working, with her hands on his. When he felt that she had the right feeling, he then said, "Now I cover you," putting his hands over hers, using the same method he had stumbled onto with Reeve Darling's assistant. Beyond that, no words, only the transmission of movement and feeling. In this way, Betty learned how to work with the entire body in one afternoon. She became his "Ichiban" that day, his number one student, and she soon went on to become the prime instrument for the future spread of Milton's work. She proceeded to work on Dub every day for the following thirty days to consolidate her learning, and thereafter took a table wherever she went to give lectures and demonstrations.

Milton and Emily were ecstatic over their reception at Esalen. For almost forty years, like Moses wandering in the desert, he had waited for the promised land of acceptance. He had tried to show his work to many doctors. He had gone to medical school, at great pains, to gain the credibility to teach his work to doctors, but he had been consistently ignored or laughed off as a quack. He had just about given up trying, before this trip, feeling with some bitterness and anger that his work was destined to die with him. Then, at age 67, he unexpectedly discovered his students, in a place he had never heard of, in an environment completely foreign to him. Yet somehow he recognized these students as his own and accepted them. He and Emily felt their sincerity, their curiosity and willingness to accept something new and different.

Esalen invited Milton to return in the Fall to conduct a full workshop in his method, following the resounding success of his first visit. He came back in November to direct the first Trager training. Eight people were invited to attend, including Betty, Dub, Will Schutz, and Gail Stewart (Dick Price's sister-in-law), who would later become another of Milton's four original instructors. Betty sponsored and helped to plan the training and assisted Milton and Emily throughout their stay. That training, over a five-day period, changed forever the way massage was done at Esalen. It also set Milton firmly on the path of teaching his approach to others. With this new door opening, Milton's optimism returned. He wrote to his sister about his relationship to Emily and the future, "...it won't be long before I will be able to help many therapists and doctors in my classes and writing....I wish everyone could have this. There is such a closeness and fullness of life together. Now Sarah, I'll accept your expression of many years, "'Lucky boy'."

He returned to Hawaii, but this time with the firm intention of closing his medical practice and devoting himself to doing and teaching the work that was dearest to his heart. He did not close the practice for another two years, in part out of affection for his longtime and devoted nurse Michiko, who would not be eligible for full social security benefits until then. But he began to conduct trainings on the mainland twice a year, according to the plan he and Betty had made during the first training. In June of 1976, he conducted his first public training in Marin County, north of San Francisco. Betty had given many sessions and made dozens of calls to recruit the thirteen people who attended that training; they included doctors, psychologists, and practitioners of Ida Rolf's Structural Integration method. The students left so excited that they immediately organized another training for their colleagues, which Betty sponsored the following week in Mill Valley after Milton and Emily had returned from a quick trip to see family in Miami.

In the Fall, Milton was back in Marin teaching. There he abruptly announced that Betty was going to be his first instructor. When she protested that she didn't have any idea what she was doing, he calmly replied,"That's okay. You learn better when you teach." A few months later, after seeing her demonstrate the work, the director of Getting In Touch invited Betty to teach the school's entire staff, including Carol Campbell, a staff teacher who had also attended the demonstration. Getting in Touch was a massage school in the Santa Cruz mountains south of San Francisco where many psychotherapists and bodyworkers came to study. Betty soon became a frequent instructor there. When she sent Milton photos of the workshops at Getting In Touch, which, like Esalen, taught massage in the nude, he fired back his reaction,"Get them back in their pants!"

Ultimately the school's owners invited Milton there to conduct an intermediate training, although no one knew what "intermediate" meant. He came nevertheless, in the Fall of 1976 and Spring of 1977, adding this new site to his teaching rounds. When he finally shut down his Waikiki office, Emily had a class organized to begin in their apartment the very next day. Now Milton had three regular places to teach; he continued that routine for the next several years. Between classes, he worked on clients in his home, using the special table that had been his tool for so many years in his office; he played golf, went to medical education seminars, and socialized with a few friends. He was happy, even if his goal of teaching doctors and finding acceptance in the medical community was as far away as ever.

By 1978, some of his students began meeting to discuss the forming of an association that would add structure and create guidelines for what had been up to that point a completely informal process. There were no standards for students, for the trainings, or for instructors. There were practically no words at all. After their training, students were given no more guidance than to go out and work on thirty bodies in the following thirty days; at that point they were considered practitioners, whatever that might mean. They were on their own. In teaching "intermediate" classes to students who had studied with him before, Milton was now being challenged to find more words to answer the many questions they raised in their confusion. In response, as he internally explored the feelings that alone had directed his hands for the last fifty years, he began to accumulate a few simple words and phrases, seemingly vague but as close to his inner experience as he could make them. He would continue to use them for the remainder of his teaching years, and they would be repeated countless times by his students, very often to the perplexed and uncomprehending looks of their clients.

In 1979, the owners of Getting In Touch flew to Hawaii for additional training, along with Betty and a few others. They wanted to give Milton a permanent place on their property to teach his work, and they wanted Carol Campbell to be named a Trager instructor. The trainings were going well; Milton was in demand, and it was time for decisions to be made about the future. Betty and Milton agreed that Carol would become the second instructor, but the proposal to have a permanent training site at Getting in Touch was never realized. Milton cared nothing about organization or administration; he simply wanted to do the work and teach it, so it would fall to others later on to create a structure that would both protect the work and allow it to expand.

In the meantime, new students kept arriving, magnetized by rumors of Milton's extraordinary hands. A young member of the massage crew at Esalen, Deane Juhan, had sat open mouthed in the first row of the audience at one of the demonstrations there. He had been working on his Ph.D. dissertation at the University of California at Berkeley before stumbling onto Esalen, where he soon abandoned his former life and took up residence once he discovered he had a knack for massage. He studied many methods of bodywork and quickly became expert. But when he saw Milton at work, he knew immediately that this was the best he had ever seen. He also rapidly concluded that no one else could ever learn to do it.

He took a couple of classes and then abandoned it until two years later, when he saw Betty giving a session. Someone other than Milton had indeed learned to do this work. He begged her to get Milton back so that he could study more, and he went to the next training at Getting In Touch. Milton hated his work. When he saw him working, he would bellow from across the room, "Stop what you're doing. Don't touch that leg. Just wait till I get over there." Or he would slap his hand away or elbow him aside. Deane called it the worst ego scouring he had ever had. At the same time, he saw underneath Milton's rough teaching style a profound kindness and benevolence. He just wanted his students to get it right. Deane literally fell in love with this strange teacher; the tall, handsome, and confident young man was not the first or the last to burst into tears in a Trager classroom. But he was the first and only member of the massage crew to abandon all the other methods he had learned and, like Betty, devote himself entirely to Milton's work. Deeply inspired, he would go on to become an instructor, teaching anatomy not only for Trager students but for massage and other bodywork practitioners throughout the United States. His book on the anatomic and physiologic effects of this work, *Job's Body*, would later become an accepted reference work for bodyworkers everywhere.

Numerous other students, from psychologists to engineers to massage experts, felt their lives opened and changed by their profound personal experience of Milton and his work, and they wanted to become practitioners of his art. Already by 1978 the work was travelling beyond the borders of the United States, first to Canada and then to France when Michel Meignant, M.D., a well-known sex therapist in Europe, became so struck with the possibilities of the work that he invited Milton to do a training there. A training in Sweden soon followed. Things were moving fast.

9

Hooked Up

The practitioners circle slowly around the room in single file. Milton stands in the center of the circle, watching them walk, sensing the feeling of their movements. A scribe stands near him, ready to write down his words, to preserve his thoughts and their changing expression. "You are surrounded by a force, a life-giving, life-regulating force....Walk about, don't spend a lot of time getting into it; it's right there, at your shoulder, a step beyond relaxation....It is nothing more than a feeling."He brings his arms up part way and opens them outward, letting them drop slowly with a gesture of submission. The words cascade down like sand spilling softly from an opened palm. Memories cascade down, too.

> He is being lifted up, up behind the proscenium arch of the Bryn Mawr Theater, a boy who is a counterweight to the heavy curtain. The colors and movement of the dancers swirl below him. His small size and frailty and the dreariness of life on the Chicago streets outside are far away now as he rides higher, above it all. An intoxicating feeling.

The practitioners continue around the room, concentrating, wanting to pick up his feeling and give him what he wants from them. They want to feel more of the "hook-up" Milton is insisting on; they want to learn these Mentastics, these mental gymnastics, the way he intends for them to understand. Cathy Hammond, who has helped him write a lyrical, meditative book on the subject, is here with him. So is Maryann Zimmermann, who organized the recent International Trager Conference in San Diego. Carolyn Mason, too, who assists at virtually all of his classes in Southern California. They regard him with adoring eyes and immense caring. He feels at ease in their company, as they walk around him. "The subtle feeling of pressure in your feet can bring you into hook-up. Just feel it, be intimate with the feeling in the bottom of your feet. Feel as though the carpet is five inches thick."

> He is taking a breath in front of the post office bulletin board. He feels the air going in, his chest expanding. He feels his own interior world. The heavy mailbag is forgotten now. He takes another breath, and another. He begins to feel light, lighter; he is the breath itself.

"Now kick your leg out slightly before you come down, with a subtle snap. It's just a little nothing. Make your muscles bounce, your thigh muscles. Let the leg dangle out of the hip socket; when you kick, it's as though the heel were dropping down into the ground. You are reaching areas of tension in the low back and all the way up to the shoulder blades. I want you to walk this way the rest of your lives, and you'll never have back problems. Put your hands on your hips so you can feel the muscles bounce as you walk. How free? How free should it be?" One practitioner lands too forcefully with each step. "Too positive," Milton gently corrects him. "What's half of that?"

> He and Sam are on the beach in Miami. "Let's see who can jump the highest." "No, let's see who can land the softest...." And what is softer than that? What is soft? How soft can it be? The beach crowd and its sounds disappear, as he is absorbed in answering this question with his athletic body. Or is it with his mind? The question resonates and reverberates within him, twining like a simple curve that repeats itself into an arabesque of infinite complexity.

Milton lifts his right forearm and hand and lets them drift gently down to his side. The practitioners imitate him. Again he lifts and lets them fall, and again. "It'll fall by gravity, you don't have to make it fall. Pause, ask 'how did it feel?' Feel the weight and it will get lighter. Heaviness and softness are not opposites. Feel the weight of the thumb. Feel it shimmer your arm as it moves. Oh my, I'm in hook-up. What is freer? What is freer than that? Coming into it, coming into it. Yes. Thank you so much."

It is sunset, after his workout at the beach. The waves are coming in, gently, one after the other. He sways to the motion of the waves; he moves his arms to their softly falling motion. There is nothing but wave, motion, sunset, peace. Time has dissolved, and he has dissolved into it.

The practitioners are shifting their weight from side to side, from one foot to the other, feeling how the body responds, how their balance is naturally maintained, unconsciously. "Let it happen. Don't make it happen. This is how babies learn to walk, losing their balance and catching it until they can stay upright without conscious effort, letting the messages from their feet reach their mind, which sends back messages to the muscles." Milton gradually speeds up the shifting from foot to foot until he is doing what looks like the softest of soft-shoe dances. The practitioners move along with him, smiles widening on their faces.

He is in the gym shadow boxing. Mickey Martin is watching the youngster, so light and fleet of foot. This kid can move. He moves, moves, living inside the movement.

He has just gotten a boy with polio to walk for the first time. The boy's parents want him back in his wheelchair. 'Why get his hopes up for nothing?' they ask. There is no point in arguing with them.

He is in a Miami hotel ballroom, the big band music carrying him along. He forgets the audience; he is caught up by the music, by the passion in his moving body. He has no idea what he will do next. One movement carries him to another, endlessly, until the music stops, and the world returns.

"Let your arms open up wide. Let that opening chest be your

inspiration for expression, as if to say, 'I have so much within my-self. Here, you take some. I can afford to freely give this wonderful feeling away.' You are developing something in the unconscious mind that is freer. It's a delightful feeling. The movements are very natural. If you think it's special, you've lost it. It's a nothingness. Don't try to find it. To try is effort; you'll fail because of the effort, because then you're not in it, you're out there working on your own. There is zero effort. People are so bound up, they can't let that feeling of hook-up enter. Yet that is where we can be in this cock-eyed world of ours. We're not talking about 'one and one is two; do this and that will happen.' No; come into the feeling and it will happen. It is no more effort than a thought."

> He walks down the street near Waikiki Beach after a morning at the office seeing patients. He has done his one special treatment before the regular patients arrive, relieving the extreme discomfort of yet another person with chronic low back pain. When the patient tells her orthopedic specialist about the results, the doctor scoffs at it. How many more times will that happen? Should he even bother with other doctors? Marcella had never doubted his genius. That dear soul is gone now, but Emily believes in him just as surely as she did.

> The sound of a ukulele rises above his thoughts. His friends the beach boys beckon to him. "Come on, doc, dance for us." They love and accept this dancing *haole*, these fun-loving men at the edges of Waikiki's affluence. He cannot resist the music, can't say no to them. The music comes to him, comes into him. The feeling is there. He begins to sway to that feeling, his movements graceful, subtle. Peace comes into him.

"The movements are directed from the mind," Milton tells the practitioners as he drifts deeper into the feeling of peace where he loves to dwell. "Make up your own Mentastics; just make sure it's in the same feeling way. It isn't anything you plan. It's just a feeling you've had before. You've had a papaya – you know how it tastes – no one has to tell you. It's in the unconscious mind. It's the unconscious mind only I'm interested in. You're asking the unconscious mind, 'Well...how did it feel?' Success in hook-up depends on recall. It felt like...... Here, I'll just go into hook-up. That'll be better."

He is on the grassy lawn of Esalen, overlooking the vast Pacific. All of these people seem so open, so aware. They like what he has shown them; in fact, they love it. They want more. They want him to teach them, here in California where he has not lived for twenty-five years. Everything is fresh here, anything is possible. He feels the cool grass under his bare toes, the fresh breeze off the ocean. A feeling comes into him, a familiar feeling. He begins to move, slowly at first, then faster, running like a young boy, opening his arms wide, opening his bountiful chest to the world, remembering and forgetting everything at the same time.

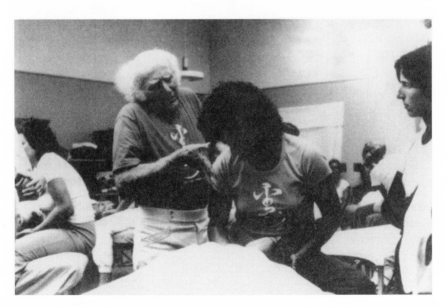

Giving the "feeling" of the work to a student, 1983

Top row: Don Schwartz, Gary Brownlee, Betty Fuller, Deane Juhan, Gail Stewart; Bottom row: Gwen Crowell, Sheila Merle Johnson, Milton, Emily, Cathy Hammond; Front: Carol Campbell

10

The Work Spreads

Don Schwartz, a short, energetic man with a passion for music, a booming bass voice, quick mind, and piercing eyes was finishing his doctorate in psychology in 1976 when his two mentors, Patricia Sun and Anne Armstrong, each separately advised him to learn Trager work. Unable to ignore these powerful signals, he signed up for his first class at Getting in Touch, with Betty Fuller instructing. Later, he could not understand why people were responding so strongly to his work and benefitting from it when he had received such brief training; he returned in the Fall for an intermediate class taught by Milton. The twenty-seven students in the class buzzed with intense excitement in their learning, and a small group of them, including Don Schwartz and Sheila Merle Johnson, channelled their enthusiasm into a series of meetings, with the intention of organizing the students into some sort of association.

Betty, who was supporting the fledgling organization financially, was swamped by this time with the paperwork generated by the trainings and hired Don at $25 a week out of her own pocket to keep the class lists and other records. Soon Sheila Merle put out a newsletter, and Betty kept it going, with Don's volunteered help. The association had been formed, but everyone was still freelancing and the work was spreading without any control. Milton was soon to name two additional instructors, Sheila Merle and Gail Stewart. Another inspired student, Cathy Hammond, was beginning to sponsor trainings in San Diego. Milton later added her, Deane Juhan, and Gary Brownlee to the instructor ranks. Canada and France wanted trainings, and larger training quarters were needed in Marin.

In 1979, as they discussed the problems growing out of this rapid expansion, Milton told Betty he wanted her to protect his name, his work, and her place as "ichiban," – number one. Although her friends were advising her not to take on the headaches of a certifying organization, she took the plunge and consulted a lawyer about formalizing the association. He drew up the paperwork needed; when he presented it to Milton on his next teaching visit, Milton was ready to sign. Betty advised him strongly to take it home, read it, show it to his lawyer. He wouldn't listen and impulsively signed the papers on the spot, giving his name and his work to the newborn Institute. So it was that in April 1980 the Trager Institute, a public benefit corporation, was formed. Betty, with the same passion that she had channelled into spreading the work of Moshe Feldenkrais, continued to oversee and nurture the spread of Milton's work, having been the first to deeply understand it and dedicate herself fully to it. Betty, Don, Sheila Merle, and Gail ran the Institute for the next several years.

As its logo, the new organization adopted a calligraphic symbol drawn and donated by Al Chung-liang Huang, a Tai Chi master and teacher with strong ties to Esalen, who had experienced Milton's work there. The dynamic and gracefully flowing lines of the Chinese characters translated to "Dancing Cloud" in English. When Milton saw the logo, one of four he could choose from, he burst out with, "That's it! That's it!" Over the years it would adorn tee shirts, pins, publications, and everything materially connected with Trager work. The Institute would later protect the use of the logo and the words "Trager" and "Mentastics" with legal service marks, in keeping with Milton's desires and out of a practical need to preserve the identity and integrity of the work. Although the work was formally referred to as Psychophysical Integration in the early years of the Institute, it later would become more universally known simply as Trager work or Trager approach. Many people also began to use the name as a verb; they routinely spoke of "Tragering" someone or being "Tragered."

Don Schwartz found office space with enough extra room to conduct trainings. In the small town of Mill Valley north of San Francisco, with Betty still covering Institute expenses, he went to work full-time as the Institute administrator instead of practicing clinical psychology, as his father would have preferred. The Institute now established membership for practitioners and a process for sponsorship and conduct of trainings to get some handle on the work, which had been spreading rapidly and chaotically at home and abroad.

Milton had flown to France in 1978 to conduct a training organized by Michel Meignant. Twelve people – psychotherapists, physical therapists, and a few of Michel's patients – gathered in a chateau at Compiegne, north of Paris, for the first European training. A Spanish physician translated, as Milton dusted off the language he had learned so many years before in Mexico.

In the class was Fabienne Hirsch, a psychotherapist who, along with her husband, a prominent surgeon, worked with Michel. She had gone through major surgery three months earlier and was severely depressed. Milton's work profoundly moved her in the most personal way. At one point he was working on her thigh, then left briefly; while he was away, she felt a softness and relaxation spread throughout her body, and she knew then with certainty that, as Milton had been saying, it truly was the mind that felt this work and changed as a result of it. When she got up from the table, she felt absolutely that she was a changed person, with a completely new body. She, too, was hooked.

The magical setting and their reception in France enchanted Milton and Emily. She participated fully in the training, taking notes and suggesting questions for Milton to help him explain his movements to the students. For the most part, however, he worked as he always did in those early years, with very few words, transmitting only the feeling of his approach. "You feel it; just do it," he said. The students were entranced but bewildered and tried desperately to help one another figure out and remember everything that he was doing. Taking notes was useless.

The French pampered Milton and Emily and treated them like royalty. Michel had rented a suite for them on the Champs Élysées after the training. Feeling a little lost in that foreign environment, they spent a few more days in Paris before returning home. Though they would not return to Europe, the memory of their experience would remain dear to them forever. Fabienne took more training from Sheila Merle and, in Betty's words, "caught on fire" and later became an instructor. She sponsored trainings in Europe for the next several years, including one that her husband Maurice attended. He, too, felt his life change as a result; he became a practitioner and began teaching anatomy courses for other practitioners in Europe.

Betty, Sheila Merle, and Gail now began travelling to Europe regularly, extending the range of the teaching. The work spread to Switzerland, then Germany, Israel, and the Scandinavian countries. Because of Michel and Fabienne's background in psychotherapy, they recommended that new students have significant therapy or other self-development experience before entering training, to be better prepared to handle the personal issues that Trager work frequently brought to the surface in their clients.

Back home, the work continued to mushroom. Although the new Institute had no program for advertising or promoting the work, enthusiastic individuals, along with Betty and Don, were getting the word out. Articles and interviews with Milton about his approach were appearing regularly in massage and holistic health journals and in the alternative press. Betty and other instructors gave demonstrations wherever they travelled, in Washington, D.C., Boston, the northwest, and elsewhere. Gail knew that other established professions gathered at annual conferences; wanting to professionalize Trager work, she organized a first international conference in 1981, which drew more than two hundred people from around the world. Students and instructors also arranged demonstrations for Milton at medical schools and hospitals in San Francisco and Los Angeles, while Betty and Don set up a tour for Milton that brought him before large audiences in Florida, Washington, D.C., Minnesota, and Ohio.

Formal medical gatherings were never Milton's milieu, and sometimes they did not go well. Milton was finally getting the recognition for his work that he had so long desired, but his simple and nonverbal style, his sensitivities, and the bitter memory of his rejections from the past all worked against him. The honesty, fearlessness, and directness that gave strength to his work hampered him in public promotional appearances.

Milton flourished when he was admired, as he was at Esalen and his other teaching venues, but he still felt the wounds from years of rejection and indifference on the part of medical practitioners. He was quite certain about the value of his work; at this point in his life, he was unwilling to try to convince others of its validity on their terms. Reverting to his old boxing defenses, he sometimes reacted to questions as challenges and tended to rebuff them with a sharp retort rather than encourage them.

Having discovered and developed his work in isolation, he was unaware of many of the body-oriented modalities flourishing at the time. If he didn't like a method, he was not shy about saying so; he frequently scorned other approaches, even when in the presence of those practicing them. In Washington, D.C., to an audience of chiropractors, he openly criticized their work. Some of the group marched out in anger. At the University of California at San Francisco, speaking to a group of physical therapists, he scolded them for being too closed-minded and incapable of understanding his work. He was not asked to return.

Among physicians, old frustrations surfaced more than anger. Deane Juhan accompanied Milton to a demonstration at Saint Francis Children's Hospital, where he greatly helped a girl with muscular dystrophy. The doctors asked questions, but he was unable or had no desire to articulate answers in the scientific and academic terms they wanted. In Los Angeles, he demonstrated his work to the renowned rehabilitation specialist, Dr. René Cailliet, who greatly admired the work and said he must write it up for a medical journal. When Milton sent him the article he had prepared, before submitting it for publication, Cailliet told him he would never get it published. "When you do your work it is scientific; when you write about it, it is philosophical," he told him. Before long, Milton gave up all promotional work and went back to his teaching, fed up once more with words as a tool to communicate the feeling nature of his approach.

Even in the classroom, among his adoring students, Milton often was rough in those early teaching years, especially when students with experience in other approaches tried to use them in his presence. "Don't do that," he would yell gruffly. "If you are here in my workshop, just do what I am doing!" As Deane had recognized earlier, this style, which offended some people, obscured his profound humility and pure intent. He wanted his students to fully understand that it was not they who were accomplishing the work through their effort and ability, but instead, they should be humbly allowing the mind of the receiver to produce a change. Fabienne also realized how much humility the work required. "If I think it is me, it is not true." With many other techniques, the practitioner thinks "I am really doing something for you." The proper attitude, a harder one to integrate, she recognized, was, "If something happens, thank you; if not, it doesn't matter."

Despite these difficulties, his teaching was in great demand; the organization and Milton were being forced to change in response. The Institute moved once more before locating, in 1983, the site it would occupy for the next nine years, in the education wing of an Episcopalian church in Mill Valley. That space became the main site for all trainings in California, and by now there were classes almost monthly. Bringing the training in-house improved the Institute's finances, and it prospered. When the classes grew too large for the church space, a meeting room at the local Howard Johnson's Motel was rented. Don Schwartz was developing into an accomplished administrative director, while other Institute organizers, now assembled as an official Board of Directors, approved a formal training and certification track for students that had been developed by a group of practitioners, instructors, and tutors led by Natasha Heifetz. Certification required two preparatory classes with required post-training fieldwork, tutorials, and recommendations. Practitioners could now advance through training levels from one to five, with Milton now teaching only the advanced classes and his special reflex response work.

Milton changed more slowly than did the Institute. He had no financial or administrative involvement in the Institute and received money only for classes he personally taught. As others continued to admire his work and idolize him, he finally recognized that his life's work was being accepted, and he grew more secure and relaxed. At last he was not alone, and though the community of students that had accepted him with such love was not the one he had expected or originally wanted, he began also to more fully accept his own students. While he enjoyed the admiration of his students, he always sternly insisted that they not speak of him as a genius, healer, or guru. "All I have is a talent," he would say. To those who were in awe of him, he responded, "I've just been at it longer," with a shrug of casual indifference.

When Milton met Moshe Feldenkrais, Betty's friend and teacher, at the Mandala conference in 1982, his vision of his own work and its place in the world changed again. Moshe's work had preceded Milton's at Esalen and elsewhere and had prepared Betty to recognize Milton's gifts. While there may have been some professional competition between them, when the two came together they connected instantly. They each sat in the front row to watch the other's demonstration at the conference, and they hugged and arranged a time to work on each other. For the first time in each man's professional life, and nearing the end of life, they had met a true peer. Here were two men about the same age, both of Russian Jewish parentage, who had each independently uncovered fundamental principles of human movement and psychophysical change through the slow and painstaking exploration of their personal awareness of body movement. Each of them had developed a system to help people change, and each of them had led varied and interesting lives.

What made them most alike, perhaps, was the deep, even mystical, reverence for the body and mind and the mind's capacity to change the body. Betty, a student of both teachers, described Moshe's attitude toward every person he worked with, an attitude similar to Milton's: "That which is within knows more than I ever will. It has been here since the beginning. That's who I am addressing. Respect that, come in quietly, wait for the right time. Say what you have to say, let them consider it, and work together."

Moshe was better able to receive help from others than his new colleague was. When Milton worked on his shattered knees, Moshe exclaimed,"New knees, new knees! We should have met years ago; you could have helped me so much." But Moshe, though he did impeccable work, was not able to get through to the tough and still resistant Milton.

In the midst of a heavy teaching schedule in Mill Valley in the Fall of 1984, Milton and Emily rode the ferry to San Francisco one day. The weather was gorgeous, and everything looked beautiful. He turned to Emily and told her he thought they should move to the Bay area. Emily tentatively raised the possibility with Betty, who was rightly concerned with the abruptness of this decision and their adaptation to the relatively severe Bay area weather after almost thirty years in tropical Hawaii. But the center of their sphere of activity and gratification was now California. Hawaii had begun to seem like a remote outpost. Brushing caution aside, Milton, in his direct, impulsive way, consulted a realtor and located a condominium that very day. It was settled. They would return once more to Hawaii to teach a final class there, pack their belongings, and take up residence in Tiburon, near Betty's house and the Institute. They wanted to be close to their family of students, sheltered in its loving arms.

By December they were ensconced in their waterfront home and were busy teaching a full schedule of classes. Students, instructors, and friends came to visit and care for them; Milton, who had always worked throughout his life, relaxed enough to adopt a family of ducks at the bay, which he fed daily, and Emily shopped and kept up the house. They did not know that they were about to suffer through one of the worst winters in San Francisco history. They never warmed up that entire season, and they were ready to move again once it ended. After a brief visit to Milton's family in Florida, they did move, this time to a small Mediterranean-style home in a gated community in Laguna Hills, south of Los Angeles. A new set of students and instructors now came to visit and attend to them, but it was a smaller group than in northern California.

Once settled in Laguna Hills, with a nearby motel as his main teaching facility, Milton virtually stopped travelling, except to the Institute-sponsored international conferences and one final trip to Florida in 1988. He installed his trusty table in a small room of the house and did treatments there, usually on people with difficult problems who had been brought in by their regular practitioners for special help. He devoted himself almost exclusively to teaching now, working with the growing number of students around the world who thirsted to spend time in his presence.

His approach was beginning to grow beyond him as an individual. To many students who had never seen him, he was becoming more of a symbol than a real person. With more instructors and tutors now certified by the Institute, many students and practitioners worked for years without ever experiencing the master's touch. Students were starting to develop strong loyalties to their primary instructors rather than Milton. The Institute had videotaped many of Milton's classes and demonstrations. Instructors used edited versions of a few of these tapes to give students a sense of his inspiring presence and manner, if only a two-dimensional one. With Cathy Hammond, he wrote what was to be his first and only book, a lyrical and poetic description of Mentastics. The book projected his image further, with its many photos of Milton moving in the graceful, light, and joyfully feeling way that he had personally taught others to experience for almost sixty years.

He was nearing eighty, and his teaching style was finally beginning to change as he aged. Where once he had astounded students with his vigorous, athletic, and large tossing movements, turning rigid bodies into vibrating jelly in seconds, he now focussed more and more on the projection of feeling. Over and over he would say it was not technique but feeling that was all-important. His patience and kindness and sweetness with students grew. Coming into a class-room, or approaching a person on the table, he embodied and projected so completely the feeling of peace and the possibility of development of mind and body that everyone in the room could feel him instantly. His work became as subtle and clear as light. Often now, instead of moving the body, he simply swept his hands slowly above its contours, projecting the feeling of smoothness, open-ness, elongation, and ease. Or he would move a leg, an arm, or neck once, twice and let it rest. He knew instantly where the person's blocks and rigidities were, and he now went there without hesita-tion, often dispensing with the routine sequence of movements that other instructors had adopted as their teaching standard.

His communication to the mind of the receiver became ever more direct and unobstructed. He sometimes did nothing more than rest his hand on the belly or chest of the person on the table, yet the impact was profound and immediate. The person arose from the table a little uncertain about what had just transpired but feeling completely changed and at peace. "This is just the beginning," Milton would say. "What you have felt you can never lose. It's not for the moment."

The sensitivity that Milton had so highly developed over the years permitted him to feel what was happening in the entire room while he worked with perfect focus on a person lying on the table. In the midst of his work, he might turn to an anxious or troubled student twenty feet behind him and say a word or two that brought instant relief or a sudden insight. Even the Mentastics had changed. He now told the students to simply walk in a continuous circle as he stood in the center, feeling the quality of their movements, nodding with approval at some, speaking softly to others: "not so strong;" "let it go;" "more indifferent." In a few minutes he had the group harmonized into a feeling of deep calm that stayed with them throughout the training.

The Institute, meanwhile, was struggling through the growing pains that any such organization experiences. How many instruc-tors should there be? How to handle a complex international corporation whose members speak different languages and are forced to travel great distances for trainings and tutorials? How to protect the name"Trager"so that only Institute-certified practitioners and students could use it? How to avoid liability when the work is used therapeutically for people with medical conditions? How to be businesslike and efficient and practical when the main purpose of the work was to develop feeling?

Don Schwartz and the Board of Directors grappled with these issues throughout the 1980's. They had kept the finances impeccably, and they had successfully won the right to protect Trager work with a registered service mark, but they also realized that if the work was to continue growing and developing, it had to emerge from its cocoon of feel-good isolation and take a stronger position in society. The Institute began to communicate with other similar organizations, and in 1991 agreed to become a member of a newly formed Federation of five established bodywork and massage organizations, and to cooperate in several areas: support for research in these approaches; development of standards of practice; development of legislative action; cooperation with health care providers; and creation of new opportunities and markets for practitioners.

By this time, Trager practitioners in more than twenty countries and forty-six American states were branching out and adding their individual talents and perspectives to the core elements of the work. Those who were already licensed as psychotherapists, physical therapists, physicians, nurses, or in other professions were beginning to find ways to integrate the Trager approach into their work settings. Many other nonlicensed practitioners, however, were finding it hard to establish full-time private practices, given the intricacies of health care payment and the continuing difficulties of verbalizing the work clearly and promoting it effectively. The future felt exciting yet uncertain.

In 1990, Milton suffered a stroke, which left him with a permanent right-sided weakness, slurred speech, and some of the symptoms of Parkinson's disease. It was a tremendous blow to a man who knew his own body so intimately and had taken care of it so well and for so long. He felt it as a kind of personal defeat and grew depressed. Shunning standard physical therapy in favor of his own self-help methods, he improved very slowly and experienced many setbacks. He and Emily realized that they could no longer maintain their home. Milton sold the flashy red Mustang convertible he had driven for years and moved with Emily into a nearby retirement community, Heritage Pointe, where their meals were prepared and assistance was near at hand.

While their physical needs were now better attended to, they deeply felt their loss of independence, and they missed the companionship of younger people, which they had always cherished. Practitioners and students called frequently, and many from southern California came to visit and help, but they had their own lives and practices to tend to. The Tragers were feeling isolated, especially Emily, who had to manage most of Milton's personal care. Their new neighbors were pleasant and welcoming, and some of them sensed the uniqueness and power of this taciturn man and his colorful wife, yet they would never fully understand or appreciate that, outside the walls of their community, thousands of men and women were being helped daily by the work he had developed, and that thousands of practitioners and students around the world felt blessed by their connection with him.

Milton grew more inwardly focussed and withdrawn, while Emily became progressively more distraught over their situation. He often just rested now, his eyes closed to the outside world, his head rocking to a distant rhythm, to a music inaudible to those around him. Still, summoning resources from unknown depths, Milton continued to teach. He needed a walker to get around at Heritage Pointe and had to take long rests during the trainings, with reminders by Emily or an assistant to sip his protein drink and take his medications. When it came time to teach, however, he somehow transcended all physical and psychological limits and again became simply the Master at work. Using skills honed over sixty-five years, he compensated for the deficits left by the stroke and his parkinsonian symptoms so expertly and subtly that most students would never know the power and will behind that achievement.

With love and deep respect in their eyes, they only saw him move gracefully, if slowly, from table to table, working on people, guiding the students, projecting the feeling of relaxation and peace with utter simplicity and directness, without a single unnecessary or wasted movement. Everything now was projection, direct communication to the mind; he moved the body hardly at all. He watched more now, and directed less, accepting the limitations of his students and his own limitations, trusting the process and the abilities of other instructors and tutors, as he moved toward an ever-more profound and fundamental letting go.

For the first time in his life, too, he was able now on occasion to accept help from his oldest and most trusted students. His doctor prescribed two Trager sessions a week for him. Local practitioners now came to give him sessions when they could, using their beloved teacher's own approach to help him as best they could. Ever the teacher, he more often than not arose in mid-session from his table, now installed in a tiny office in the apartment, to give them pointers. In his characteristic way, without a word, he simply brushed the table with the back of his hand, directing the practitioner to lie down. Soon those silky hands, soft as a cloud, began their dance, rocking the body back and forth, back and forth, lulling the conscious mind, opening the body, returning it to the deep, eternal source of peace.

The Trager Institute's "Dancing Cloud" logo, painted by Tai Chi Master Chunliang Al Huang

11

Principles of The Trager Approach

"Alas, our theory is too poor for experience"
ALBERT EINSTEIN

"No, no! Experience is too rich for our theory"
NIELS BOHR

To commit the principles of Milton Trager's approach to the linear and neatly subdivided printed page is to exclude automatically the effective expression of one essential principle: it is at the core a feeling experience. Milton has little faith in the capacity of the written or the spoken word to convey the feeling at the heart of his work. "Put enough words together and you have a book," he swiftly summarizes his bleak view of the value of words in truly understanding that experience. Yet, the spread of his work to the larger community, where words and explanations are critically important, has been slowed by the lack of an organized and systematic elaboration of its underpinnings. Milton views verbal exposition of his approach as useful only to the extent that it stimulates people to seek out the feeling experience embodied in the work.

The following description, then, is presented for that purpose, and to assist the reader in understanding how the realm of feeling can produce positive changes in health, well being, and medical practice. The principles will be divided into five sections: The Approach; The Sources of Change; The Source of Problems; How the Process Works; and Technique. Technique is presented last because Milton considers it less important than other aspects of the work and because it cannot be learned adequately from a book.

The Approach

Trager work is an approach to people and their problems, rather than a method that can be learned by memorizing facts, procedures, symptoms, or remedies. The approach of the practitioner is the same regardless of the problem, symptom, or diagnosis of the receiver. At the same time, each person's individuality is fully and intimately appreciated because the practitioner directly feels the physical tissue and its individual responses. Every word, gesture, and touch of the practitioner, every aspect of the relationship with the receiver, is meant to convey and evoke the desired outcomes.

"It is the *manner* in which I touch," says Milton, not the technique, which is important. To an extent unusual in therapeutic work, practitioners must embody the very qualities they wish to convey to, and nurture in, the receiver. Thus, practitioners can be successful only to the degree that they have developed themselves. The approach is easy, light, soft, and free, and gracefully moving. It is not goal-oriented. The practitioner enquires, expecting an answer but never demanding one, "How should it be...?"

The Sources of Change

The Life-Giving Force

Individual practitioners do not produce change. Rather, they tap into the life-giving, life-enhancing, life-regulating vibratory force or energy, far greater than the individual, that surrounds us, ever-present, nearby, and accessible to both practitioner and receiver. Whether one names that energy life-spirit, God, Chi, or creative inspiration does not matter; the source is nonsectarian, the name unimportant. It is the source of human sustenance, of homeostasis and healing, and thus also of change.

To draw a parallel from what is known in physics, we are surrounded by vibratory waves of many kinds, such as gravitational, subatomic particle, light, and sound waves. Vibrational energy at regular frequencies, when applied to physical particles, can organize them into beautifully ordered patterns called standing waves. Structures in which standing waves are present vibrate at their most natural and easily sustained frequency. Such structures are said to be in resonance. When another similar structure, or oscillator, vibrates at the same frequency, the energy transfer between them is optimal and they form a perfectly articulated resonant system.

Hook-up

The Trager practitioner, and any other person, can tap into this vibratory energy or force by adopting a meditative state, which Milton refers to as "hook-up." He makes no distinction between this state and deep meditation, and he insists that it is only from this state that effective work can emerge. The practitioner's development also advances whenever he or she is in that state. The feeling of deep peace that comes from being fully absorbed in watching a beautiful sunset or a newborn baby are other everyday examples of hook-up.

The practitioner waits until he or she enters this state before beginning to work on another person and seeks to stay in this state throughout the work. In such a state, the practitioner is able to be intuitive, creative, dynamic, alive, and vibrant, peaceful but not passive. It is an altered state in which resources greater than those contained within the conscious, thinking mind are accessible, similar to the way a person may use hypnosis or visualization or dreaming states to reach internal resources beyond thought and analysis.

Practitioner as Channel

The practitioner, in an altered yet connected state, feels the receiver's body in motion and at rest and engages in a self-enquiry. What are the qualities of softness, lightness, ease, freedom of movement, and vibrancy? How should the body feel? How should it move? How should it be? The answers are relayed through the practitioner's mind – as feelings – to the mind of the receiver, and the body changes accordingly to the extent that the connection between the two is realized. Although the hands of the practitioner touch the receiver's body, it is the mind of the practitioner and that of the receiver feeling the information flow that allows the body to change.

The practitioner's goals, thoughts, ambitions, and analyses must be put out of the way, because none of them can make a fundamental change in the other person. "I'm just there," says Milton. "I'm lucky." To his students he says, "Be there with the person. You stay out of it."

Returning to parallels in the field of physics, one can say that the practitioner, tuned to a desirable frequency through the state of hook-up, forms a resonant system with the receiver, and there follows an optimal transfer of energy. The relationship between the two is thus essential. As the physicist Henry Stapp said of the elementary subatomic particle, "It is, in essence, a set of relationships that reach outward to other things."

The Mind

The mind records the experiences of individuals throughout their lifetime: perceptions of the external environment, internal sensations, physical activities, and emotions. Patterns of response develop unconsciously, particularly those connected to feeling states, and the memory of these former experiences arises in realms beyond conscious thought. Response patterns include bodily motions, all of which involve muscle action. But the muscle tissue does not act independently. Whether the responses are reflexive, as when a baby develops balance and coordination by responding to neuronal messages transmitted from the contact of the feet with the ground, modifying its response until it can stand and move forward, or whether they are voluntary, as when one purposefully raises an arm to reach an object, they originate in signals sent to and from the central nervous system. Emotion-activated responses likewise originate from processes within the mind.

The Source of Problems

Learning Harmful Patterns

Response patterns may be learned or conditioned, or they may be brought about by biological stress, in what Hans Selye called the General Adaptation Syndrome, wherein very similar bodily events take place in response to a host of very different stressors. An individual may develop response patterns that initially were necessary for survival or for maintaining homeostasis but that later become unnecessary and even harmful.

A given individual may also develop problematic response patterns due to abnormalities or damage in the physical, psychological/emotional, or spiritual domains. In the physical domain, accidents or other injuries may alter response capabilities by producing direct organic harm. Genetic or other systemic abnormalities may also prevent or alter bodily responses. Furthermore, the body may compensate for such damage in a way that, over time, may produce additional damage. For example, people favoring an injured knee may alter their walk protectively in such a way that they develop hip or back pain. And both of these mechanisms – the direct injury and its compensations – can alter responses to other external and internal stimuli that have nothing to do with the original damage or its compensatory sequelae.

Emotions such as anxiety, fear, depression, or anger likewise produce characteristic response patterns with bodily correlates. People in such states, in fact, are rather easily recognized by their body language and expressions. When these emotions become fixed or chronic in an individual, harmful psychological and physical patterns may result. The weakness and hopelessness characteristic of spiritual loss—although it may be given other names—may likewise be visible in alterations of response and in abnormal patterns of physical and psychological behavior.

Muscle Tension

Perhaps the simplest way to generalize about many of the bodily alterations described above is to think of them as producing changes in the state of tension in the muscles and connective tissue. While hormones and other biochemicals are involved in such changes, much of the net effect can be seen in muscle activity. Comprising the greatest single component of the body's mass, muscle not only holds the body together and powers all of its movements but also pumps the oxygen-rich blood that feeds the cells, and it regulates the flow of blood in the arteries that it lines. Without the muscles that keep the eyes moving, we could not see. Without the muscular peristaltic motion of the gastrointestinal tract, we could not digest and eliminate.

Muscles have a resting tone and they also contract and relax to produce their actions in the body. If the resting tone or the coordinated contraction and relaxation of muscle tissues are inappropriate to the needs of the person, problems inevitably develop. Excess muscle tension may, for example, produce constricted arteries, pain, discomfort, imbalance, loss of body movements or dysfunctional body movements, and excessive response to messages from the external and internal environment, in an escalating or vicious cycle.

Insufficient tension may also produce imbalance, loss of body movements or dysfunctional body movements, as well as weakness and inadequate perception and response to messages from the internal and external environment.

The state of tension, then, is a response to the inner and outer environment that may be conditioned and patterned by past events and perceptions. The barriers to positive change lie in the mental response patterns that produce the muscle response, and those barriers are composed of past physical, emotional/psychological, and spiritual events.

Trying to alter patterns of tension by the use of great personal effort frequently adds to problems. Where there is already excessive tension, using effort only reinforces the pattern of too much activity.

Where there is insufficient tension, great effort overpowers the diminished capacity of the body to perceive a stimulus and mount a response to it.

How The Process Works

Breaking Patterns

"Nothing can change until the old pattern is broken," says Milton. To mount appropriate and life-enhancing responses to messages from inside the body and from the outside world, one must first break the old response patterns. But the breaking need not be a violent, aggressive act – and it should not be – when the old pattern is one of excess tension, because such violence only reinforces the use of excessive effort to maintain the homeostasis of the body. Working "hard" creates and sustains tension. There may be temporary relief when the body and mind are worked to the point of exhaustion, but the fundamental pattern is not changed in this way.

Even when the old pattern is one of too little response – too little tension – as in paralysis or other conditions where weakness predominates, trying hard produces more tension than the weakened tissues are able to respond to. First, the practitioner must help the receiver to perceive small external and internal sensations and to develop a minimal response to that smallest of stimuli. Once a minimal response is elicited, the old pattern is broken and the new pattern can be bolstered and built on.

Feeling Something Better

The receiver must first feel something different and better in order to establish and develop a different and better pattern. If I am always anxious, I cannot change fundamentally until I have felt calm and peacefulness. If I am uncomfortable, I cannot change until I experience comfort. Once I have experienced a better sensation, the possibility of returning to that improved feeling state will always be available. Psychologists would refer to this approach as fostering positive change through state-dependent learning, memory, and behavior, a kind of conditioning in which associations may be developed between feeling states and bodily functioning. By returning to a positive feeling state that has become associated with improved function, the body then automatically returns to its improved functioning. This new learning counteracts body learning received under more stressful conditions that may have become associated with bodily tension, holding, guarding, or weakness and paralysis.

Mind to Mind Feeling

Thinking about comfort, relaxation, peace, and ease of movement is not the same as feeling them, although the mind is used in both thinking and feeling. We can regard feeling as the ground state out of which the thinking, planning, and analysis functions of the mind emerge. But to "feel" feeling is another kind of experience. When the mind and body are at rest and in peace, we experience a feeling state that is evident not only to us but to those around us. All of us can sense the presence of a person who is internally comfortable and at peace; the feeling that person exudes can even be contagious. In the Trager approach, the contagiousness of such a state is used purposefully, and therapeutically, by the practitioner for the benefit of the receiver. It is brought close through touch and other sensations, the better to be transmitted to the mind of the receiver, where it is felt and "caught" and where it produces corresponding changes in the body.

The Tissues are "Dumb"

Muscles, connective tissue, and bone do not think; they merely sense and relay their sensations to the central nervous system. Changes in those tissues are directed by higher centers of the organism. The changes can be instantaneous, brought about by a reflex arc to and from the spinal cord, or by thoughts, desires, and feeling states. And the muscles and other tissues become servants to those messages from the higher centers.

How Should It Be?

Practitioners use their own state-dependent learning and memory to bring about personal changes in their body states. By asking internally and recalling the state of peaceful, relaxed, and light, free movement, their own bodies respond, becoming soft, graceful, easy, and comfortable. Even the enquiry must be made easily, without demand but with the expectation of a response, to facilitate retrieval of the desired feeling state. And the same questions are asked in relation to the receiver, while messages of free, easy, soft, smooth, pleasant, effortless, balanced, responsive, and graceful motion are continuously and repeatedly being transmitted to the receiver. What is soft? What is light? What is free? And what is softer than that? And what is lighter? What is freer?

It's Like the Measles

"You catch it from someone who has it," Milton says. A feeling can be as contagious as a yawn. The practitioner loads the atmosphere with the "virus" of relaxation, peace, and flowing movement. Every action, every word, every touch is filled with it, until the receiver catches it and "comes down" with it.

Recalling the Feeling

"I was lying on the table and I felt really good and it felt like.......Well.., how did it feel?" Like a hypnotic suggestion, the recollection of the feeling of the Trager approach brings with it the entire experience and the desirable behaviors associated with it. Sometimes the act of asking the question is enough by itself to bring the recollection; at other times, a simple movement of an arm or a leg in the manner it was moved during a Trager session reproduces the experience throughout the body. Each time the feeling is recalled, the body reproduces the improvements it learned when that feeling was initiated. The more often recall is used in this way, the easier it becomes to return to the more desirable state.

No Technique

The Trager approach is based on feeling and response. If nothing is felt, then nothing happens. Once something better is felt, it may be completely unnecessary to touch the receiver or teach anything. While standardized movements are taught and commonly practiced, they are never routinized. Each person brings a different body and a different history. The practitioner feels what the receiver brings and acts accordingly, responding only to what he or she feels. When a positive response is felt in the receiver's body, then the work is accomplished. That may take an hour or a second, one session or many, depending on the development of the practitioner and the nature of the problems the receiver brings. New movements may be created on the spot if they are appropriate to the unique individual receiving the work.

Technique

With the foregoing caveat on technique in mind, it is possible to introduce and describe specific ways the practitioner works using the Trager approach. But no amount of technique produces change. Techniques and movements have been developed because they help the receivers to pick up feelings and change themselves in a positive direction.

Structure and Function

First, the approach is functional, rather than structural. While practitioners learn anatomy and use their knowledge of it, their goal is not to re-align or reposition the body. They want the receiver to be able to perform any and all movements comfortably, painlessly, and pleasurably. They constantly observe and feel what is moving and what is not, how it moves or does not move. They seek an easy balance rather than a so-called "right" posture, which often produces unnecessary muscular tension. Thus, the approach is free-form and seeks to free the form of the body. It is for that reason that the Trager Institute has as its logo the Chinese characters that represent a dancing cloud.

Pain

The Trager approach is painless. The receiver is instructed to notify the practitioner of any pain that is produced or increased during a session. The many people who live by a "no pain/no gain" worldview, or who are otherwise accustomed to tolerating pain, often find this an extremely difficult instruction to comply with. In addition to their basic desire to "do no harm," which is inherent in their approach, practitioners exclude pain from the work so as not to reinforce the harmful patterns that receivers bring with them. Pain produces guarding, which is tissue tension.

After a session, the practitioner cautions the receiver not to look for the pain. Often when there is pain relief as a result of the work, the receiver immediately wants to see how far he or she can move a previously painful part before the pain returns. This again reinforces the harmful pattern and undoes some of the just-completed work.

Tablework

The two major components of the approach are tablework and movement education, which Milton calls Mentastics (mental gymnastics). In the tablework portion, the receiver lies on a padded table wearing loose clothing, or undergarments only if the person feels comfortable that way. If the receiver finds it hard to lie down, it is possible to adapt this portion of the work to the sitting position or other positions. The practitioner may work on a problem area and related parts only or may do a full-body session lasting up to one and a half hours. In a full-body session, the receiver begins in the supine position. The practitioner typically works first with the head and neck, moving then to the lower limbs, followed by work on the belly, chest, and arms. The receiver then turns over, and the practitioner works the back of the lower limbs, then the shoulders, back, and pelvis. The receiver turns over once more, and the practitioner finishes by returning briefly to the head and neck.

Mentastics

Before or after the tablework session, or both, the practitioner demonstrates and has the receiver learn and practice some extremely simple movements designed to recreate the feeling of the tablework movements. These then can be used at any future time to help with specific problems or to evoke the relaxed and freely moving state felt during the session. Some practitioners offer regular Mentastics classes to small groups, without the tablework component.

The practitioner may use verbal imagery to help the receiver get the feeling of the movement. All movements are accomplished in an easy and playful way, without effort or undue emphasis. The practitioner draws from specific movements that Milton has taught or devises new movements and images to fit the needs of the receiver. All of the movements are designed to make the receiver more aware of body and mind sensations. They promote balance, grace, and coordination, and they reinforce feelings of elongation, lightness, and easy looseness.

Mentastic movements are not exercises in the traditional sense. There is no specific number of repetitions, no specific length of time to practice them. As in the tablework, once the response is felt, the job is done. The movements can be used easily during the day. They require no special clothing or equipment; they are generally small and subtle and thus do not attract undue attention. Their purpose is to evoke the positive sensations that allow the body to move comfortably and easily.

Feeling the Tissue

During the tablework, the practitioner assesses and treats at the same time by feeling the body tissues. The tissue should feel light, soft, and vibrantly toned, almost fluffy to the touch, throughout the body. It should move easily. Practitioners use their entire hand to encompass and give security to every area that is touched; the hands are soft sensors that impart the very feeling that the receiver's tissues should have. Movement is initiated by the practitioner's entire body, not by the muscular activity of the arms alone.

Feeling the Weight

The capacity to feel body weights, the practitioner's and the receiver's, is essential to the effectiveness of the practitioner. The improvement of the receiver depends also on the development of his or her capacity to feel body weights, to become intimately familiar with them, especially during the Mentastics work. The practitioner lifts an arm or a leg and feels the weight of it. If the receiver unconsciously uses muscular activity to prevent gravity from letting its full weight rest in the practitioner's hand, then the practitioner has more work to do. Throughout the session, the practitioner feels the weights of the body. When they are fully in hand, then the tissues are relaxed. Likewise, the practitioner constantly attends to his or her own body weights, appreciating their relation to gravity and balance, using those weights to maintain personal comfort and ease and convey those qualities to the receiver.

In the Mentastics work, the practitioner teaches receivers to feel their own body weights and how to give the weight up to gravity at will. This is one of the most difficult lessons to learn for those who are convinced they must use effort to accomplish anything important. Letting the lower limb drop out of the pelvis, letting an arm simply fall to the side, may be profound and novel experiences for many.

The Weights "Feed" the Hands

While continuously feeling the weights of the body, the practitioner begins to set them in motion during the tablework.

The head is rolled side to side, or the leg is rolled, or the arm is swung, always in the directions of natural body movement, and only within the range of motion where the movement is free and easy. Sometimes the free range of motion is extremely limited; sometimes there is no range of motion. In such cases the practitioner returns to feeling the weight until a spontaneous release by the receiver allows the possibility of greater motion.

Each time the practitioner moves a body part in one direction, he or she allows that part to return by its own momentum and weight. That same weight, once in motion, can be used to sustain movement in both directions with very little action on the part of the practitioner. It can be used as well to extend the motion further, once the receiver's muscles release to allow the extended motion. The moving weight of parts of the body also sets other parts in motion, like a resonant wave rippling outward. A legs rolling back and forth on a table, for example, sets the foot into a free waggling motion. The momentum of that leg and foot "feeds" the hands of the practitioner. Before long, it is as though the body is moving itself without any effort by the practitioner. Such internally generated and effortless motion allows more and greater releases by the receiver, and greater motion, until the body is moving with complete freedom.

Finding the Body's Rhythm

Big bodies move differently from little bodies; big body parts move in a different tempo than small parts. Practitioners feel for the most natural frequency of the part being rhythmically moved, and they move in sync with that frequency, forming a resonant system with the receiver that allows optimal energy transfer. The rhythm lulls the receiver into a calm and peaceful state, so that the conscious mind does not interfere with the letting go of the tissues. Frequently, a receiver who is unused to letting go in this way tries to consciously anticipate and control the movement, to "get it right." Practitioners feel this unneeded effort immediately, as it causes the rhythm to break and fragment. They then return to smaller motions until the rhythm is re-established.

The lulling rhythms often bring back to the receiver some of the earliest sensations of infancy and childhood, as the rocking – especially of the back and pelvis – continues. Years of tight holding patterns often fall away as the rhythm works externally and internally, until the body comes to rest, calm yet alive and vibrant.

The Integrating Wave

Trager movements, in the tablework and during Mentastics, are characteristically curving and wavelike, without clear edges and boundaries. They are smooth and they are smoothing when they touch the receiver's body. They elongate and they expand and open out away from the midline. They rock, they roll, they shimmer the tissue and make the muscles bounce lightly. They open the joints through gentle traction and by allowing body weights to be acted on by gravity.

Most importantly, Trager touch and movement integrate the different parts of the body, and they integrate mind and body through feeling. Practitioners notice how the movement of one part affects and resonates with other parts of the body, and they work toward that integration from head to toe. In the tablework, for example, the practitioner moves from shoulder to back to pelvis to shoulder to back, joining them in feeling, giving receivers a sense of their body as a unified and coordinated whole.

Mentastics movements are likewise never jarring or abrupt, but always graceful and smooth. While walking, the person's feet sink into the ground with a rolling motion or touch it lightly as the body casually shifts its weight from side to side. The person is taught to rise from a chair with the flow of the incoming breath, to lift an arm and let it flutter down in a gravity-drawn spiral. Each such movement allows the person to experience the unity of all the body parts.

What is Half of That?

The Trager practitioner uses less to produce more. The approach increases body awareness, opening the mind to greater subtlety of sensation. Where there is excessive tension, excessively forceful action, an appropriate self-enquiry is,"What is half of that?" And the same question can be asked after each repetition of a motion. It is a useful question for the practitioner and the receiver alike, as both are prey to modern life's overly emphatic, goal-oriented, and pressured style of accomplishment. The most natural vibration, the most resonant frequency, no more than that, is the right amount. Adding to it does not improve it. How much energy is required to offset the effect of gravity? And what is half of that? All motions become more balanced, graceful, pleasurable – and more efficient – when such awareness is present; yet it can be the most difficult thing to teach. Here again, the practitioner imparts it by embodying it.

Resistance

In the opening session at one of the International Trager conferences, a practitioner pleadingly asked Milton for help. "Lately I've been bumping up against resistance," she said, introducing her topic. Milton interrupted her, "Well, stop bumping up against it." Confused, she tried to continue. "But what do I do?" she persisted. Without a moment's pause, Milton replied, "Say 'excuse me'".

When there is resistance to movement, practitioners do not break through it. They simply do less, until nothing remains to be resisted. At that point the body typically lets go and more movement becomes available. The message of safety and security is thus continuously delivered and the response is not long in coming.

Tightness and Looseness

As with resistance, the tighter and harder the tissue, the lighter and softer the practitioner works to encourage change, until the messages of lightness and softness are picked up by the receiver and the tissue responds by loosening and softening. With a person who is too loose – that is, where there is weakness, flaccidity, or even paralysis – the practitioner evokes reflex muscle activity. The practitioner evokes a response by providing the lightest of resistance, sending a message of tension until the receiver's capacity to resist is activated. The necessary tension is then reinforced by repeated messages coming from different directions. This gradually conditions the receiver to respond appropriately to signals from the environment that require resistance.

Repetition

During the course of a Trager session, the practitioner sends thousands of sensory messages to the receiver. This almost boring repetition lulls the receiver's conscious mind away from inappropriate resistance or over-control; at the same time, it conditions appropriate responses. The mind and body learn unconsciously through such repetition, just as a pianist learns a piece by patterned movements of the hands and fingers repeated countless times and carried along by rhythm. The patterns so conditioned are specific to the parts of the body that need them the most.

And It Felt Like...?

The practitioner teaches the receiver to evoke the new and positive patterns in the future by recalling feelings rather than by recalling specific motions or exercises. This is done when the receiver is in a calm and receptive state, whether after Mentastics or after tablework. Typical verbal messages include the following: "You were lying on the table and it felt like........what did it feel like?"; "Yes, this body"; "This arm."

The manner of recall is essential for evoking the feeling. Neither the practitioner nor the receiver asks with emphasis or force, but casually, almost indifferently, with a kind of idle curiosity that bypasses the conscious, thinking mind. The receiver then can use recall at any and all times to reproduce the better feeling in a specific body part. Furthermore, recalling the feeling in one area usually produces that feeling throughout the body. In that way, one simple and hardly visible movement of a hand or even one finger can recreate the entire Trager experience. And that experience is never more than a feeling away.

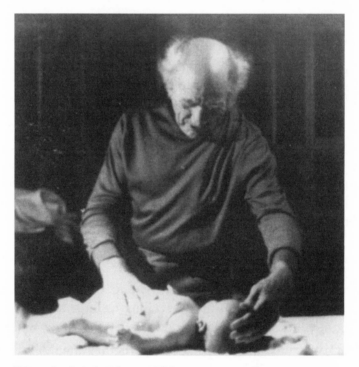

"Tragering" Avie Schutz, 1976

12

Moving Medicine

*...in the history of human thinking the most fruitful
developments frequently take place at those points where two
different lines of thought meet.*
WERNER HEISENBERG
Physics and Philosophy

*'By science I assume you mean full satisfaction of the mind
arising from sufficient evidence, that kind of science?'*
'What other kind is there?'
JEREMY LEVEN,
*Satan: His Psychotherapy
and Cure By The Unfortunate
Dr. Kassler, J.S.P.S.*

The principles of the Trager approach contain elements that are no-
tably absent in contemporary medicine. Specifically, modern medicine lacks a clearly stated unifying principle understandable in the
language of the average person; thus it appears fragmented and
behaves that way. Conventional medicine gives too little credence
to the potential for healing and to a power, greater than science
itself, which both the clinician and the patient can access and use. It
shuns feeling as an avenue to improved health. It eschews touch as
a therapeutic tool and tends to use movement therapeutically only
in the form of strength-building exercise.

The current state of medicine is, of course, but one point on its
long evolutionary path. But the explosion of knowledge in the sciences, particularly in this century, has led to a dizzying rapidity of
change in medical thinking and medical care that confuses and over-
whelms clinicians and patients alike. Most medical educators
realize that much of the knowledge they impart to students today
will likely be proved wrong within a generation.

Probably the greatest and most influential knowledge explosion in this century has emerged from the field of physics. The development of physics since Albert Einstein has altered forever our scientific view of the universe. Werner Heisenberg, as the discoverer of the uncertainty principle – one of the concepts critical to the development of the new physics – fully and sympathetically appreciated the difficulties we would face in remaking our understanding of reality, in light of the new discoveries. *In Physics and Philosophy,* he described the role of modern physics in human thinking in relation to the rigid framework of nineteenth century conceptions of science, which had guided us previously. He wrote specifically of the differences between scientific language and what he referred to as "natural language."

"This frame was supported by the fundamental concepts of classical physics, space, time, matter and causality...Matter was the primary reality. The progress of science was pictured as a crusade of conquest into the material world. Utility was the watchword of the time.

"On the other hand, this frame was so narrow and rigid that it was difficult to find a place in it for many concepts of our language that had always belonged to its very substance, for instance, the concepts of mind, of the human soul, or of life.

"...one of the most important features of the development and the analysis of modern physics is the experience that the concepts of natural language, vaguely defined as they are, seem to be more stable in the expansion of knowledge than the precise terms of scientific language, derived as an idealization from only limited groups of phenomena. This is, in fact, not surprising, since the concepts of natural language are formed by the immediate connection with reality; they represent reality. It is true that they are not very well defined and may therefore undergo changes in the course of the centuries, just as reality itself did, but they never lose the immediate connection with reality. On the other hand, the scientific concepts are idealizations...through this process of idealization and precise definition, the immediate connection with reality is lost.

"...Whenever we proceed from the known into the unknown, we

may hope to understand, but we may have to learn at the same time a new meaning to the word 'understanding.' We know that any understanding must be based finally upon the natural language because it is only there that we can be certain to touch reality, and hence we must be skeptical about any skepticism with regard to this natural language and its essential concepts. Therefore, we may use these concepts as they have been used at all times. In this way modern physics has perhaps opened the door to a wider outlook on the relation between the human mind and reality."

Modern medicine, as practiced in America and other technologically advanced countries, remains encased, in large part, by the conceptual frame of the nineteenth century. Shunning the uncertainties that are integral to an understanding of quantum physics, it divides the body into distinct parts and systems and focusses on linear causes and effects and linear specific treatments, introduced from outside the individual, for those parts that are considered to be diseased. Its specialized technology and sophistication have lost correspondence with the natural language of health, with the idea of wholeness out of which the word "health" arose and toward which modern physics once again points us. One need look no further than a standard textbook on medicine in the United States, *Harrison's Principles of Internal Medicine*, to discover that it contains no definition of the word"health."The same is true for most other medical specialty texts. The question "What is health?"is not asked in most medical school curricula. How then is a doctor to know when the patient is healthy?

The word "mind," so prominent in natural language throughout history, is likewise largely ignored by many medical specialists and its domain given over to psychiatrists and other therapists who, in turn, often ignore the physical body. While most doctors no longer use the derogatory term "It's all in your mind" to dismiss patients whose problems they cannot understand or solve, that phrase encapsulates the attitude still held widely in the medical community. Others in that community are hoping that new discoveries about the brain and its neurochemistry will make the problems of the mind

as definable and treatable as problems in other body parts and systems. Of course, there are individual physicians who attend to both
mind and body, and one specialty, Family Medicine, which attempts
to include both in its purview, but they are in the minority.

The integration of body and mind, then, has been left substan-
tially to those who work at the margins of medicine or beyond. But
the large number of people crowding along those margins today
implies that there is increasing pressure for change. That pressure is
viewed by many in the medical community as a regression away
from science and toward more primitive views of the world. But
others see it as a positive movement into a new paradigm for medicine, one that corresponds with natural language and with the new
understanding of reality which advances in modern physics have
helped to bring about.

In 1993, the New England Journal of Medicine reported the results of a survey which showed that one in three Americans uses at
least one type of unconventional therapy. Extrapolating the results
to the entire U.S. population suggests that there are more visits to
unconventional therapists annually than there are to primary care
physicians (general internists, family physicians and general practitioners, and pediatricians). People make those visits for problems
such as headache, back pain, and other chronic pains, which are also
the most common complaints they bring to conventional doctors.
Only thirty percent of the people making such visits informed their
regular doctors; this fact prompted the researchers to observe that
there is a deficiency in current doctor-patient relations and to rec-
ommend that doctors should inquire about these therapies when
taking a medical history. The people using unconventional therapy
tend to be young and well-educated and to have high incomes.

There are important reasons beyond curiosity and unresolved
ailments that drive people away from conventional scientific
medicine. While science is touted as the key to understanding and
controlling the forces of nature for the benefit of man, people most
often experience their relationship with scientific medicine as a loss
of control. When physicians cloak themselves in the white robes of

authority or are unwillingly clothed in them by their patients' expectations, that feeling is intensified. But even the thoughtful and partner-like physician, trained in science, realizes that science cannot explain most of the ailments human beings suffer, nor can it cure them. If the doctor tells the truth about this, patients realize that the hoped-for mastery of the doctor is an illusion.

The typical physician uses medications or surgical techniques to treat the patient; these are complex outside forces poorly understood by patients, which act on them in unknown ways, outside of their control. Rarely are patients told – rarely is a doctor taught – that any healing power or control lies within them. By using marginal therapies, people are acting in part to keep alive in their minds the potential for healing and control. That potentiality is often closed off by the many dead ends of conventional scientific medicine, in much the same way that, in subatomic physics, a scientific observation of an event causes the wave of probability to collapse, leaving only one stark and often unsatisfying reality.

The three most commonly used forms of unconventional therapy in the United States are relaxation techniques, chiropractic, and massage. The first is clearly an approach that joins the body and the mind and the latter two utilize touch and manipulation. All three focus on the feeling part of the patient. This finding implies that the deficiency in doctor-patient relations is a quite specific one and not merely a problem requiring doctors to take a better medical history, as the authors of the New England Journal article imply.

While many hundreds of articles on the therapeutic use of relaxation training for a wide variety of conditions have appeared in the medical literature over the years, physicians have been slow to fully incorporate this therapy in day-to-day clinical practice. When it does occur to them to prescribe such training, they rely largely on physical therapists or biofeedback technicians to do the teaching.

In the late 1920's, Edmund Jacobson, in his book *Progressive Relaxation*, gave the time-honored use of rest as a therapeutic modality a more scientific basis. His technique, along with Autogenic Training (which is better known and more frequently used outside the United

States), remain the principal tools for relaxation used by physical therapists and others today. Herbert Benson, as a professor of Medicine at Harvard and a believer in the benefits of Transcendental Meditation, gave therapeutic relaxation a boost in the mid-'70s with his book, *The Relaxation Response*, which spawned many additional research studies. In more recent years, biofeedback training has emerged as a new tool to teach patients relaxation skills; the computer technology and measurable changes associated with its use helped it to find favor within the scientifically-oriented medical community.

The majority of physicians, however, are not comfortable with what appears to them to be too "soft" a science. They do not commonly prescribe relaxation training for their patients and even less frequently do they teach it themselves. It is a skill that they rarely learn in medical school or in their residency training, despite the sizable medical research literature that supports its use.

Most physicians use touch and movement only as a means of making an assessment and diagnosis or in conducting an invasive procedure. Very often that diagnostic or probing surgical touch elicits pain purposely or incidentally; almost always it is done with cool professionalism so as not to suggest an inappropriate intimacy. Psychotherapists, on the other hand, are usually prohibited by law or by professional practice standards from touching their patients; touch is considered to be inappropriate when one is working with the mind.

To say that doctors and patients are out of touch with each other, then, is to do more than use a figure of speech; it is to state the literal truth. This is not a criticism of doctors. They, like the general population in technologically advanced societies, have lost direct personal awareness of the body and its connections with the mind. When Ashley Montagu, the anthropologist, began reflecting about touch in 1944, the skin – the largest organ of the body – was a neglected subject. His 1953 paper, "The Sensory Influences of the Skin," stood virtually alone in its field. By the time he published his landmark book, *Touching: The Human Significance of the Skin*, in 1971, there were hundreds of research papers on the subject. Although Montagu knew that psychosomatic medicine was already a well-established field of study, he was fascinated specifically by what he termed "the mind of the skin," and he was convinced of its far-reaching effects on human behavior. Those research papers and their significance have yet to be fully incorporated into the consciousness of the medical profession. In fact, in mid-1993 a search of the medical literature revealed no new clinical articles written on the effects of touch in the previous five years, except in nursing journals.

In the realm of the mind, Wilhelm Reich, a psychiatrist and student of Freud's, broke with his mentor by using physical touch to crack the physical armor that he believed was connected with psychological problems. His radical approach was rejected by most of his colleagues, but he influenced the development of a host of body-mind integrative approaches. Both of these pioneers shed new light on body-mind connections. Such connections are generally appreciated and utilized in the medicine of traditional cultures but were mostly abandoned in technologically advancing societies during the development of mechanistic science since Newton's time.

So far the word "mind" has been used in its natural language form, without defining it, as Milton Trager does not define it. But a sense of its application in health and in medicine can be understood by exploring the ideas of the biologist and philosopher Gregory Bateson and other thinkers. It was Bateson, the bent and crippled 6'5" physical and intellectual giant, who had joked after personally experiencing Milton's work at Esalen,"Dr. Trager, you've grown shorter!" He believed that our society's view of reality had to shift from seeing the world as a collection of objects to seeing it as a set of relationships. This idea had grown, not out of the study of physics, but out of his study of patterns in nature.

"Bateson proposed to define mind as a systems phenomenon characteristic of 'living things'... In Bateson's view, mind is a necessary and inevitable consequence of a certain complexity that begins long before organisms develop a brain and a higher nervous system. He also emphasized that mental characteristics were manifest not only in individual organisms but also in social systems and ecosystems, that mind was immanent not only in the body but also in the pathways and messages outside the body...According to Bateson, the organizing activity of a living system is mental activity and all of its interactions with its environment are mental interactions....mental process being immanent in matter at all levels of life." Fritjof Capra, who studied with Bateson and summarized his views in *Uncommon Wisdom: Conversations With Remarkable People*, went on to draw further conclusions, as a result of these conversations.

"...since all self-organizing activity is mental activity, the process of getting sick and of healing are essentially mental processes. Because mental activity is a multilevel pattern of processes, most of them taking place in the unconscious realm, we are not always fully aware of how we move in and out of illness, but this does not alter the fact that illness is a mental phenomenon in its very essence."

These conclusions are echoed and expanded in the theoretical basis for Sensory Integration, a system developed by the occupational therapist A.J. Ayres, who, like Milton Trager, was stimulated by her work with children with cerebral palsy to develop her innovative ideas. In *Sensory Integration: Theory and Practice*, Fisher, Murray, and Bundy describe the relationship of the mind to what they call the brain-body.

"When we speak of causation between the mind and the brain-body, we are not referring to the simple linear form of causation with which we are all familiar...In the case of the mind and the brain-body, we are referring to other more complex forms of causation. Complex causation is more properly understood as a given set of events that create possibilities and potentialities for a person to mentally experience something...the mind serves to integrate, and give order to, sensory information from the body and the environment that is being processed in the brain...the mind and the brain-body articulate at holistic levels."

In stating that illness and health are essentially mental processes, Capra notes that "we move in and out of illness." Movement is inherent in the process. This idea is congruent with energetic principles of health and illness, such as the traditional Chinese principle of "chi," which forms the basis of its medicine. It is congruent as well with our knowledge of the universe, which from the macro level of galaxies to the invisible level of subatomic particles and light waves is in constant, rhythmic motion.

Modern physical therapy literature also appreciates movement, as noted, for example, in *Human Movement*, an introductory text by Galley and Forster. "All people move constantly...it is through their movements that people have the ability and the means to interact with their environment, express their feelings and relate meaningfully to one another." But physical therapists do not attempt to elevate that notion to the level of a unifying principle of health and illness. The closest our scientific medicine comes to a unifying principle of health and disease is in the idea of homeostasis, a kind of dynamic balance, yet ironically the word itself contains the contradictory idea of stasis, or lack of movement. More importantly, the principle of homeostasis is not used by physicians as a unifying principle in their day to day work with patients, nor is it typically taught to patients in the course of their medical treatments. Carl Simonton, the maverick cancer specialist, in his conversations with Capra, even objected to the question"Are we healthy?" To him, the more appropriate question for patients and doctors is "Are we moving in a healthy direction?"

The realm of feeling is used even less than energy, mind, or movement as a unifying principle of health and illness, but there are indications that it plays a far greater role than we imagine. Our natural language hints at this. "How are you feeling?"we say. "I feel good." "I feel sick; I don't feel well." In current research its role appears again in the conception of the unified mind-body and life itself as an information system. A product of cybernetics and systems theory, this view holds that biology is at its core a process of information transduction. Ernest Rossi, a psychologist, reviews the research and discusses the implications of this perspective in *The Psychobiology of Mind-Body Healing*. The following summary draws largely from his work.

Rossi focusses on the limbic-hypothalamic system within the brain as the major anatomical link between mind and body. The pea-sized hypothalamus, the prime organ of the autonomic nervous system, lies in the center of the constantly changing limbic system. Limbus, meaning "border," conveys a sense of this system's location and hints at its function, lying as it does between the so-called higher and lower centers of the brain. The hypothalamus receives signals from and sends signals to all parts of the nervous system. As the major communication pathway of the limbic system, Rossi writes, "It integrates the sensory-perceptual, emotional, and cognitive functions of mind with the biology of the body." If these integrated functions combine to run our biology, then feeling – as in sensation and emotion – takes on a much greater importance than it has been credited with in the past.

The emerging importance of feeling helps to explain the well-known, but poorly understood, placebo response. For decades clinicians have known that patients respond positively to placebos in a wide variety of medical conditions. Yet, for the most part, their effects have been brushed aside as insignificant and idiosyncratic, as another indication of problems being "**only** in the mind." Careful research, however, has shown that the placebo response is probably a general ingredient in all clinical situations. What is more, there are indications that it may account for as much as 55% of the benefit of all healing procedures. The response itself seems to consist largely of some combination of patients' beliefs, expectations, and feelings in relation to their problems and to their interactions in the clinical environment.

Anatomical and physiological research on the hypothalamus has revealed that within it lie powerful centers of pain and pleasure, the great conditioners and reinforcers of behavior. Hans Selye's research on stress demonstrated further that mental experience led to physiologic reactions that are characteristic of the emotions and that such reactions, when they persisted, would lead to severe medical problems. In addition, many different kinds of experiences were found to produce the same physiological responses, leading Selye to his formulation of the General Adaptation syndrome. His research and those of others later pinpointed certain hormones, peptides, and neurotransmitters as the agents that produced these responses.

Those chemicals are the same ones that help to encode memory and learning. J. McGaugh, a physiological psychologist, concluded from his research that hormones released during an experience affected the strength of the memory of the experience, and that the limbic-hypothalamic system modulated those influences in conjunction with neurochemicals at the periphery. Such findings suggest that memory, learning, and behavior are highly dependent on the emotional and sensory state of the individual at the time of their experience. Other research supports the idea that automatic stimulus-response connections, or habit patterns, also conditioned by experience, are more basic than cognitive processes and that they operate not only in humans but at all levels of life. Such habit patterns help to account for the persistence of symptoms, which Selye had noted long ago.

Rossi proposes a state-dependent theory of mind-body communication and healing, expressed in four hypotheses.

1. The limbic-hypothalamic system is the major anatomical connecting link between mind and body.

2. State-dependent memory, learning, and behavior processes encoded in the limbic-hypothalamic and closely related systems are the major information transducers between mind and body.

3. All methods of mind-body healing and therapeutic hypnosis operate by accessing and reframing the state-dependent memory and learning systems that encode symptoms and problems.

4. The state-dependent encoding of mind-body symptoms and problems can be accessed by psychological as well as physiological...approaches – and the placebo response is a synergistic interaction of both.

If memory, learning, and behavior are state-dependent, then what a person experiences in a certain feeling state will tend to be associated, perhaps forever, with that state. There are fascinating examples of amnesia in the literature on hypnosis in which forgotten events could be recalled only when subjects were brought back into the same, sometimes traumatic, feeling state they were in at the time of the event. In medical and other psychological literature also, research has shown that people more easily recall what they have learned when they are in the same state and environment in which they did their original learning.

Rossi's third hypothesis – that all methods of mind-body healing operate by accessing and reframing the state-dependent memory and learning that encode symptoms and problems – explains how movement, touch, and feeling help to unify and heal mind and body. Each time the state-dependent processes are accessed, there is an opportunity to reframe the problem in a way that helps to resolve it. His teacher, the late psychiatrist and hypnotherapist Milton Erickson, described this process as he used it in his method of hypnotic psychotherapy.

"The induction and maintenance of a trance serve to provide a *special psychological state in which the patient can reassociate and reorganize his inner psychological complexities* and utilize his own capacities in a manner in accord with his own experiential life...Therapy results from an *inner resynthesis* of the patient's behavior achieved by the patient himself. It's true that direct suggestion can effect an alteration in the patient's behavior and result in a symptomatic cure, at least temporarily. However, such a 'cure' is simply a response to suggestion and does not entail that reassociation and reorganization of ideas, understandings and memories so essential for actual cure. It *is this experience of reassociating and reorganizing his own experiential life that eventuates in a cure*, not the manifestation of responsive behavior which can, at best, satisfy only the observer."

Erickson's description, coming from the perspective of an entirely different field, bears an astonishing resemblance to the principles and methods that underlie Milton Trager's approach to the mind and body, and it also highlights several of the principles already discussed in this chapter. Erickson affirms the self-organizing and integrating capacities of the mind. He asserts that true change comes from within the patient, not from an introjected cure. And he uses a special psychological state – trance – to facilitate the reorganization and resolution of problems. Although not described in the quoted passage, Erickson's contributions to hypnotherapy included the development of the indirect approach and utilization techniques. He never fought against the patient's resistance but instead worked with it and utilized whatever the patient presented in order to induce and facilitate change.

It is possible now to briefly "reframe" some of the principles of the Trager approach in relation to the ideas presented in this chapter. The intent of the approach is to connect body and mind while recognizing that it is the organizing, integrating mind that is of primary importance. It utilizes an altered feeling state, called "hook-up," that accesses universal energies and puts both the practitioner and the receiver in a peaceful and relaxed frame within which new learning can be introduced and remembered. The practitioner helps the receiver develop the skill needed to recall that altered state and the learning that was gained while in it. The practitioner does not impose a "cure" from outside and does not fight the resistance of receivers but rather utilizes what is present in their bodies at the moment and suggests indirectly how the body should feel: lighter, freer, easier, softer, more fully and gracefully moving.

The practitioner acknowledges the receiver's inherent power to make self-healing changes. The Trager approach uses the vast sensory capacities of the skin and deeper tissues to transmit messages, through modalities missing in conventional medicine – touch, movement, and feeling. Using wavelike, moving rhythms that are at the core of all forms of matter and life, it communicates its message thousands of times during a session to break habitual patterns associated with the receiver's problems and to establish newer, more positive patterns of relaxation and movement, well-being and peacefulness, and pleasure in the feeling of the body and its movements. In the process, the feeling of relaxation and peaceful pleasure help to harmoniously regulate the nervous system and move the individual in the direction of health.

Milton and Emily

13

Trager Approaches

a body changes
its mind theory doesn't
matter i feel your form
moving at the heart
of all that matters
light soft here
and there it is
coming home

Today the margins of medicine are moving – philosophically, economically, and socioculturally. In recent years, new ideas and methods, and old ones, have gained increasing, if sometimes grudging, acceptance in conventional medical thinking and practice. Chiropractic, relaxation therapy, biofeedback, massage, acupuncture, homeopathy – all have found small or large niches while conventional medicine continues to develop and use its sophisticated technologies and methods for diagnosing, preventing, and treating illness. At the same time, economic pressures are dramatically altering the landscape of medical practice and forcing clinicians to change their views of medicine.

In 1989, the Rodale Press, which publishes alternative health and self-care books and magazines for the lay public, produced a volume called *Hands-On Healing*. It describes alphabetically, from Acupressure to Trager, no less than thirty-eight different therapies involving use of the hands, a bewildering variety to be sure. Other books, magazines, and newspapers are popularizing some of these methods with increasing frequency. But what is the actual and potential role of the Trager approach, both in medical and nonmedical settings? Where does it fit? Who are its practitioners? This chapter tells the stories of a few individual practitioners and the people and institutions they serve, and it describes the changes that their work has helped to produce in people's lives and in the way our health care system operates.

An unusual characteristic of the Trager Approach is the intimate connection its practitioners feel with the work and its originator, even if they have never met him, and how much personal pleasure they get from doing the work. The connection is through feeling. Just as Milton Trager had to first feel what he wanted within himself before transmitting it to others, Trager practitioners receive and are profoundly affected by the feeling of the work in the most personal way before they decide to practice it. In order to do the work well, practitioners must experience the feeling state, while they work, which they want the receiver to feel. This means that practitioners usually enjoy their sessions as much as the receiver does; giving a session is like receiving one. In conventional medicine, by contrast, no one asks doctors to experience the feeling of good health while they are treating their patients. Robin Pittman describes this aspect of the work in the application statement she submitted to the Institute to become a practitioner.

"I have found TRAGER to be extremely far-reaching in its effects. It extends so effortlessly to all areas of my life. The themes that kept coming up for me were playfulness and extending my focus to include the whole body rather than just the part I was working on. I needed to learn to be settled and quiet and playful – all at the same time. I also learned to tune in and trust my direct sensory experience of the person receiving the TRAGER session, and to extend the sensory experience of what was going on to obtain information from other areas of the body as well as the part being worked on.

"Studying TRAGER has allowed me to see myself more clearly. It has allowed me to practice, within a structure, principles that I know –such as we meet resistance by backing off – so that I could integrate that habit into my nervous system. Then I have found that it effortlessly extends to all other areas of my life. I find myself natu-

rally being more harmless, more loving, less attached to the out-
come of any situation, and more trusting in nature. I feel relief that
this trust has grown and I no longer feel that I have to fix everything. Everything gets fixed effortlessly. It has shown me concretely
how, when we let go and flow with the universal intelligence, life is
effortless, blissful, playful, fun, and fluid. TRAGER has given me a
system to tap into huge peacefulness during activity and maintain
it for longer and longer periods of time. If I forget it for awhile, I
now can easily re-acquire it through MENTASTICS movements or
even intention and memory of it...

"TRAGER has demonstrated to me how certain attitudes and
boundaries in my life simply fall away and reveal more love and
beauty. It has shown me how these attitudes and far-reaching perceptions of reality can be released in an hour or an instant, inno-
cently, when some tension is released effortlessly and naturally during a session. These are limitations that I was not even conscious of
until they were gone and I noticed that a problem that I thought had
existed simply vanished."

Mia Kusumadilaga describes the difficulty and complexity of that
process in her application statement for practitioner status. She
had suffered from severe back pain for a year before experiencing
the work.

"I was brought up to carry myself with 'good posture', which
meant that I would hold my breath, suck in my stomach, and tense
just about every muscle in my body – my jaws were tight, my neck
and shoulder muscles like hard ropes, my chest frozen, my abdominal muscles tense: no wonder I had a constant pain shooting down
my left leg!..(As I am writing this and looking back to that time, I am
appalled by my present assessment of my physical state and even
more amazed by the fact that I did not see myself that way back
then. In fact, I thought I was in good physical shape, except for my
back pains, which were too painful to ignore; they were a nuisance
and embarrassment, for I had great pride in my health and
well-being.)

"I experienced my first Trager lesson when I submitted to being a 'demonstration specimen' in my Beginning Trager Training...I was as stiff as a log and almost unavailable to new learning. But by the end of the week, I opened a crack ever so slightly and had a taste of the possibility of how I could be. It was a real beginning for me. Yet, I still did not have a sense of what it meant to actually feel my 'being' or that of a person I was working on. I was so accustomed to 'understand' and to 'do', that I exerted a lot of effort in *achieving* perfection in the *performance* of my moves. And so it was that I did not qualify for Practitioner Candidacy until I was reevaluated by Carol Campbell a month later."

Because of the personal development required, the process of becoming a practitioner sometimes takes years, as students work through their own blocks and resistances, leaving the work for a while and returning to it when they are ready to continue. Some instructors believe that no one should become a practitioner who has not done personal developmental work through psychotherapy or other methods.

Once trained, qualified, and certified by the Trager Institute, practitioners work in varied settings. Some practice as an avocation to enrich their lives, working only with friends, family, and acquaintances. Others give sessions part-time, in addition to their regular jobs. Practitioners who make Trager work their full-time occupation may have private practices or may work in, or in connection with, the offices of health care professionals, wellness centers, or alternative healing art centers. Because Trager practice is not a licensed profession, individuals practicing it must contend with, or function outside, the complex economics of established health care systems unless they are otherwise licensed already.

Many practitioners enjoy exploring new and uncharted areas of application for the work, expanding the circle of people for whom the Trager approach makes positive change possible. Reports of new applications of the approach are frequent in the community of practitioners and lend excitement to the growth of the work. By April of 1993, there were more than a thousand active practitioners and close to a thousand students working in twenty countries around the world.

Dr. David Hubbard is a neurologist, on the faculty of the University of California San Diego School of Medicine, who runs a center in La Jolla specializing in chronic pain. He also is in charge of pain management at Sharp Hospital in San Diego. Like many clinicians dealing with pain and its associated problems, Hubbard grew dissatisfied with the standard modalities available for its treatment. He felt that there must be a better way to break the pattern of pain in his patients.

In 1985, he began a systematic search for alternative modalities. He invited practitioners of various hands-on methods into his office, watched how they worked, and assessed their effectiveness. One after another came and went; none of them was quite right. Finally, in walked a diminutive woman with an exotic name – Kelsi Eno-Konya – who practiced an approach with another odd name: Trager. As soon as he saw the rhythmic movements she used and her sensitive touch, he stopped his search with two words: "That's it."

Dr. Hubbard made Trager work a regular component of his pain program, hiring practitioners to work in his office; the results were positive and dramatic, as his patients began to improve more quickly and sustain their improvement longer. His curiosity piqued, he began to wonder why this approach was so effective. He knew that it worked with feeling and the mind, and he suspected that somehow Trager work was reaching the autonomic nervous system – the system responsible for stress reactions – and modulating its responses. But most medical scientists and clinicians were saying that there was no direct connection between the autonomic system and the skeletal muscles.

He began to research the matter, collaborating with a team of colleagues and ultimately completing electromyographic studies that clearly showed the autonomic system-muscle connection and the way it influences pain. The results were published in the respected neurology journal, Spine, in 1993. The Trager approach was not only being used but some of its principles scientifically validated in an established medical setting in the specialty of neurology.

At the University of Southern California School of Medicine, the author is an Assistant Professor in the Department of Family Medicine and a physician assistant who directs the School of Medicine's Physician Assistant Program. I had become a Trager practitioner in 1989 and wanted to make the work, which I had found so personally valuable, available in this prominent academic medical center. I explained the Trager approach to the Family Physicians in my department. To my surprise, two of them already were familiar with it and liked the idea of its being brought in; the rest were sympathetic but puzzled. I then presented the approach to the Physical Therapy Department, showing a tape of Milton working with patients at the National Parkinson's Disease Center in Florida. The physical therapy faculty were interested and skeptical. Still, they allowed me to use their clinical facility for my work.

Slowly over the next several years, word of the availability of this method at USC, and its effectiveness, got around. As this is being written, my clinical schedule is full; patients with chronic headache, back, neck, and other pain, Parkinson's Disease, spasmodic torticollis, and a variety of other conditions are referred to me by family physicians, neurologists, rheumatologists, neurosurgeons, physical therapists, and occupational therapists. A brief article written for the National Parkinson's Foundation Newsletter stimulated calls and letters from all across the country asking for more information and the whereabouts of practitioners. And clinical research projects using the Trager Approach are in the planning stages.

At first I was as surprised and pleased as some of my patients when people who had had chronic, daily headaches for years were pain-free after three or four sessions, or when a woman who could barely shuffle into the room with excruciating back pain rolled off the table with a smile on her face after the first session, and when people with Parkinson's disease felt relief and relaxation they hadn't felt in many years and were able to move much more easily. After a while, I began to accept these changes as normal. The simple Mentastic movements I show patients and other methods I use for recalling the feeling of the work help them to sustain the benefits of the sessions, improve balance and coordination, and enjoy the pleasure of movement.

Adriennne Stone was a physical therapist working with outpatients at Saint John's Hospital in Santa Monica, California when she took her beginning Trager training in 1981. Soon she was using Trager work instead of other standard modalities because it was so hard not to use it after experiencing the benefits. At first she found it difficult to explain to the ordering physicians. When she asked a doctor's permission to use Trager Approach for a patient with thoracic outlet syndrome, the reply was an immediate and curt: "No!" When the patient asked his neurologist to prescribe it, the doctor said he wanted documentation of its benefits, and if there was no documentation, she should forget it. Ultimately, that physician relented, and soon physicians were prescribing it by name. Five more physical therapists on the staff learned the work during the time Adrienne remained there, and others took the training after she left.

Adrienne was also building a private practice part-time, by word of mouth. By the time she was ready to practice Trager work privately full-time, in 1990, she and the other physical therapists at the hospital were using the Trager approach for a wide variety of conditions: back and neck pain and other chronic pain, myofascial syndrome, multiple sclerosis, cerebral palsy, stroke, arthritis, spinal cord injury, pulmonary rehabilitation, and even chemical dependency. She was also regularly teaching Mentastics to groups as part of their rehabilitation. She remembers with particular satisfaction those occasions when she was able to significantly improve the quality of life of patients who had been confined to wheelchairs, in some cases for decades.

While some of the doctors and physical therapists remained skeptical, they grew to respect the work and sent many of their most problematic patients to experience this approach. The work was well enough accepted over time that one doctor who headed the pain management program convinced the hospital board to accept Trager work as a regular hospital procedure and even build a special room for it. The non-Trager physical therapists were often curious when both the patients and practitioners came out of that room beaming with pleasure and success. Like other medically oriented practitioners, Adrienne had to learn to translate her Trager work into standard medical jargon, to find a way to properly document the pleasure and relief in the medical records. Now she has a full-time private Trager practice, seeing patients referred by psychologists, family physicians, neurologists, rheumatologists, and orthopedists for a wide range of problems.

Janet Long, a Trager practitioner who is a Marriage, Family, and Child Counselor as well as a medical art therapist, practices part-time in the pain clinic of Children's Hospital Oakland in California, in addition to her private practice. As part of a multidisciplinary team, she treats children from five to eighteen years who are referred by such hospital units as rehabilitation, neurology, and hematology/oncology when these specialties have exhausted their usual pain control methods.

In Vancouver, British Columbia, the Huntington's Disease Foundation of Canada invited Trager practitioners Lhesli Benedict and Michael Madrone to a camp for people with this disease to introduce the work and give sessions. While most of the attendees were initially hesitant to sign up, once they saw how profoundly the work affected their friends, there was an immediate rush to register for the remaining sessions available.

A woman there who had not had a normal night's rest in ten years because of the jerky involuntary movements of the disease slept for two hours immediately after the session and later that night slept soundly for the first time in a decade.

In France, three physicians and several kinesiotherapists use the Trager approach in their practices. Dr. Jean-Louis Marie is a hospital-based geriatrics specialist and a Trager practitioner who finds the work important in his practice. Dr. Claire Paillard, a generalist, and Dr. Maurice Hirsch, a surgeon and sexual dysfunction specialist, also use the approach. As Trager practitioners, they keep this work separate from their regular medical relationship with patients. Dr. Hirsch observes that his patients with sexual dysfunction always have bodily problems and that Trager work consistently helps them; he finds it a marvelous tool in patient care. His wife, Fabienne, a practitioner and Trager instructor, works with him and in conjunction with psychotherapists, using the approach. Other Trager practitioners in France work as movement educators.

In Northern California, practitioner Benna Kolinsky works at the Mendocino County Community Health Clinic, using the Trager approach as a member of a team responsible for chronic pain management for indigent adults in the county, especially for those who have not responded well to other modalities.

In Athens, Greece, practitioner Sigrid Grosskopf is a professor of anthropology at the university. But she also leads Mentastics groups for university students, among others, and has presented the Trager approach in workshops for medical students at the School of Medicine.

Trager work has found its way into a host of nonmedical areas as well, where it provides relaxation, body awareness, movement education, and simple pleasure. Practitioners work with professional athletes, children, musicians, even animals. In Manhattan, Trager practitioner Roger Tolle had been giving sessions almost weekly to Marge Rivingston, a noted voice teacher whose students have included singer Linda Ronstadt and actors Meryl Streep and Kevin Kline, when she asked him to co-teach a class for her students. He describes his first day teaching.

"Marge and I and the rest of the students listened as the first student got up to sing her song. Afterward Marge asked her how it felt. It felt tight and too high, she said. Marge looked at me, asked me what I saw. And I said 'I don't know. I need to feel what's going on.' I got up and went over to the student. Not knowing where to begin, I took hold of her hand and began to set it in motion. I played with her shoulders, meeting the considerable resistance there with softer and softer hands. Then I asked her if she would begin her song again so I could feel what was going on as she sang. It was clear from her first breath that her method of getting sound out involved a tremendous amount of contained effort. So as she sang I stayed with her, feeling her breath with my hands on her lower ribs, resting my hands on her shoulders, looking for softness with my mind, holding her in Hook-Up. As the higher notes of the song came along, I supported her habitual lifting of her shoulders by lifting them for her so she could feel herself make the sound without the effort. And what a sound it was! High, clear, focussed, on pitch. And easy! So easy she couldn't believe it. And tears started to roll down her cheeks. Whose voice was that? She wanted to know. What had I done? Why hadn't it been that easy before? Could it always be that easy? What had I loosened to allow that voice to emerge, to float free?"

Roger began to co-teach regularly, warming up the students at the start of class. "I guide the warm-up entirely with questions, just like I would teach a Mentastics class. The basic question, 'What movement does my body want right now?' serves as an opener to connect mind, body, and emotions in the present moment. Then we move on to questions like, 'What feeling radiates into your chest from swinging your arm like this? What would be a softer feeling in your jaw and throat? How does your weight shifting from one foot to the other help your lower back stay fluid?' and other questions and explorations Trager students and practitioners would recognize."

Susan Hartman of Grand Rapids, Michigan works with victims of abuse, as do a number of other Trager practitioners, and leads Mentastics classes. Recently she was asked by an office furniture manufacturer in her area to work in their facility and help employees find better ways of moving in their jobs.

Louise de Montigny of Montreal, Canada works as a practitioner at the *Centre Alternatif*, a day center for people with problems of substance abuse. She was asked to describe her work there.

"In general, drug addicts are persons who are very little in touch with their body because their body was one of pain and suffering. They were obliged to attenuate this suffering through the use of artificial means such as drugs. They became used to 'freezing' all their feelings. It is therefore difficult to resume contact with this body. Therefore, I have to proceed in stages. First, I have to be capable of accepting their resistance – and there is much. Also there is much fear – fear of letting go...When you have been taking drugs for years, you forget what it is like to live a more relaxed life. Often, severance brings about a very high stress level. An enormous stress! That is why there are so many relapses...They have to be offered means of relaxation, and in this sense TRAGER is of immense help."

The practitioners described here, and many others like them, are helping to move the Trager approach out of its isolation in the marginal mist of "New Age" thinking, into the mainstream of wellness, health, and even into the established health care system. They are bringing the benefits of touch, movement, body aware- ness, feeling, and relaxation to bear – lightly – against traditional resistance to these methods. In the medical literature, evidence of the benefits of relaxation training for a variety of medical conditions has been documented in hundreds of recent clinical studies. Articles on the Trager approach have appeared in physical therapy journals. And doctors in specialties such as neurology, orthopedics, rheumatology, and family medicine are beginning to recognize its benefits.

Betty Fuller, as founding director of the Trager Institute, envisions a day when every community will have a center for touch, move- ment, and feeling, when people beginning in grade school will incorporate these methods into their daily lives, and when profes- sional practitioners will serve great numbers of people for a host of problems and medical conditions. For the time being, individual practitioners are creating their own places in health care and related fields. But there are indications that this approach, developed more than sixty-five years ago, is finally finding its proper place, and that the time has come for moving medicine.

Bibliography

Benson, Herbert. *The Relaxation Response*. William Morrow and Company, Inc., New York, 1975.

Bentov, Itzhak. *Stalking the Wild Pendulum: On the Mechanics of Consciousness*. Destiny Books, Rochester, Vermont, 1977.

Brooks, VE. "Motor Control: How Posture and Movement are Governed," Physical Therapy, v 63 n 5, May 1983, 664-675.

Bootzin, RR; Perlis, ML. "Nonpharmacologic Treatments of Insomnia," Journal of Clinical Psychiatry, v 53 n 6 (suppl), June 1992, 37-41.

Burish, TG; Matt Tope, D. "Psychological Techniques for Controlling the Adverse Side Effects of Cancer Chemotherapy: Findings from a Decade of Research," Journal of Pain and Symptom Management, v 7 n 5, July 1992, 287-301.

Capra, Fritjof. *Uncommon Wisdom: Conversations with Remarkable People*. Bantam Books, New York, 1989.

Davison, GC; Williams, ME; et al. "Relaxation, Reduction in Angry Articulated Thoughts, and Improvements in Borderline Hypertension and Heart Rate," Journal of Behavioral Medicine, v 14 n 5, 1991, 453-469.

Eisenberg, DM; Kessler, RC, et al. "Unconventional Medicine in the United States: Prevalence, Costs, and Patterns of Use," New England Journal of Medicine, v 328 n 4, Jan. 28, 1993, 246-252.

Engel, JM; Rapoff, MA; Rogot Pressman, A. "Long-term Follow-up of Relaxation Training for Pediatric Headache Disorders," Headache, v 32, 1992, 152-156.

Feldenkrais, Moshe. *Awareness Through Movement*. HarperCollins, New York, 1972.

Feltman, John, Editor. *Hands-On Healing*. Rodale Press, Emmaus, Pennsylvania, 1989.

Fisher, Anne G; Murray, Elizabeth A; Bundy, Anita C. *Sensory Integration: Theory and Practice*. F.A. Davis Co., Philadelphia, 1991.

Heisenberg, Werner. *Physics and Philosophy*. Harper and Row, New York, 1958.

Holroyd, KA; Nash, JM. "A Comparison of Pharmacological (Amitryptiline HCL) and Nonpharmacological (Cognitive-Behavioral) Therapies for Chronic Tension Headaches," Journal of Consulting and Clinical Psychology, v 59 n 3, 1991, 387-393.

Hubbard, DR; Berkoff, GM. "Myofascial Trigger Points Show Spontaneous   Needle EMG Activity," Spine, v 18 n 13, 1993, 1803-1807.

Jacobson, Edmund. *Progressive Relaxation*. University of Chicago Press, Chicago, 1929.

Juhan, Deane. *Job's Body*. Station Hill Press, Barrytown, New York, 1987.

Linden, Wolfgang. *Autogenic Training: A Clinical Guide*. Guilford Press, New York, 1990.

Lipset, David. *Gregory Bateson: The Legacy of a Scientist*. Prentice Hall, Englewood Cliffs, New Jersey, 1980.

Montagu, Ashley. *Touching: The Human Significance of the Skin*. Harper and Row, New York, 1971.

Primavera, JP; Kaiser, RS. "Non-Pharmacological Treatment of Headache: Is Less More?" Headache, v 32, 1992, 393-395.

Puskarich, CA; Whitman, S; et al. "Controlled Examination of Effects of Progressive Relaxation on Seizure Reduction," Epilepsia, v 33 n 4, 1992, 675-680.

Rachlin, Edward S. *Mysofascial Pain and Fibromyalgia: Trigger Point Management*. Mosby-Year Book, St. Louis, 1993.

Rossi, Ernest L. *The Psychobiology of Mind-Body Healing: New Concepts of Therapeutic Hypnosis*. W.W. Norton & Company, Inc. New York, 1986.

Rossi, Ernest L., Editor. *The Collected Papers of Milton H. Erickson*, vols. I-IV. Irvington Publishers, New York, 1980.

Schachter, L; Weingarten, MA. "Attitudes of Family Phyicians to Nonconventional Therapies," Archives of Family Medicine, v 2, December 1993, 1268-1270.

Scoggin, F; Rickard, HC. "Progressive and Imaginal Relaxation Training for Elderly Persons With Subjective Anxiety," Psychology and Aging, v 2 n 3, 1992, 419-424.

Selye, Hans. *Stress Without Distress*. Harper and Row, New York, 1974.

Strogatz, SE; Stewart, I. "Coupled Ocillators and Biological Synchronization," Scientific American, December 1993, 102-109.

Trager, Milton. *Trager Mentastics: Movement As a Way to Agelessness*. Station Hill Press, Barrytown, New York, 1987.

Watrous, IS. "The Trager Approach: An Effective Tool for Physical Therapy," Physical Therapy Forum, April, 1992, 22-25.

Witt, P. "Trager Psychophysical Integration: An Additional Tool in the Treatment of Chronic Spinal Pain and Dysfunction," Whirlpool, Summer 1986, 24-26.

Witt, PL; MacKinnon, J. "Trager Psychological Integration: A Method to Improve Chest Mobility of Patients with Chronic Lung Disease," Physical Therapy, v 66 n 2, February 1986, 214-216.

Witt, PL; Parr CA. "Effectiveness of Trager Psychophysical Integration in Promoting Trunk Mobility in a Child with Cerebral Palsy: A Case Report," Physical and Occupational Therapy in Pediatrics, v 8 n 4, 1988, 75-94.

Zukav, Gary. *The Dancing Wu Li Masters: An Overview of the New Physics.* William Morrow & Co, New York, 1979.

Index

For more information about Trager work, contact:

United States Trager Association
13801 W. Center Street, Suite C
P.O. Box 1009
Burton, OH 44021
U.S.A.

Phone: 440-834-0308
Fax: 440-834-0365
Email: admin@tragerus.org